D1174339

*problems in*
# BASIC OPERATIONS
# RESEARCH METHODS
*for management*

*problems in*

# BASIC OPERATIONS
# RESEARCH METHODS

*for management*

*by*

RANDOLPH W. CABELL

*and*

ALMARIN PHILLIPS

*New York · London, John Wiley & Sons, Inc.*

COPYRIGHT © 1961 BY JOHN WILEY & SONS, INC.

*All Rights Reserved. This book or any part
thereof must not be reproduced in any form
without the written permission of the publisher.*

LIBRARY OF CONGRESS CATALOG CARD NUMBER: 61-7802

PRINTED IN THE UNITED STATES OF AMERICA

# Preface

The exercises and problems contained in this book were developed for use in our course in operations research methods at the Graduate School of Business Administration of the University of Virginia. In our view, it would be inappropriate—and it may be impossible—to train future business administrators so thoroughly in the basic sciences, in statistics, and in operations research itself that they graduate with anything approaching competence in the field. They should, however, know something of the types of management problems to which O. R. may be applied and of the more commonly used concepts, tools, and techniques. It is the manager, not the operations research team, on whom problems are thrust. The failure of the manager to be at least cognizant of the nature of O. R. may constitute a serious deficiency for the business administrator of the future, since his ignorance would likely mean that an O. R. approach is not attempted.

We are convinced that even a vague appreciation of the powers of the O. R. method, just as a similar appreciation of mathematics and the sciences, cannot be gained by reading the exposition or by following through the experiments of others. A modicum of individual problem-solving is a minimum requirement for most students to understand the sometimes elusive methods and to appreciate the need for building models to fit problems rather than to search for "cookbook" solutions. The problems presented here were designed with this pedagogical intent. The topics covered include several mathematical programming methods, a variety of inventory models, queuing problems, problems requiring Monte Carlo analysis, sequencing models, replacement problems, assignment problems, and—because of their frequent omission in business school statistics courses—problems in the design of experiments and the analysis of variance.

In terms of numerical complexity and the required level of mathematics, most of the problems are simple. None requires the use of automatic computing equipment though a few could be handled more easily or more completely if such equipment were available. Elementary differential and integral calculus are required to solve some. Some knowledge of probability and sampling theory, of the normal, Poisson, and negative exponential distributions, and of the chi-square test is helpful. We have found, however, that students who lack formal training in these subjects are usually able to handle the problems with only a small amount of additional instruction.

Requiring students to solve these exercises and problems in conjunction with readings from O. R. textbooks, periodical literature, and actual cases offers business administration students an opportunity to gain a fairly concise idea of what O. R. is all about. They should learn something of its capabilities and something of its language. This is perhaps as far as the neophyte decision-maker should go to avail himself of the enormous contribution which O. R. may make in the future.

We would like to thank Dean Charles C. Abbott and the Sponsors of the Graduate School of Business Administration at Virginia for allowing us both the time and the resources necessary to prepare this experiment in business education. We also appreciate the conscientious work and valuable criticism of our students who suffered through early versions of the problems. Finally, our sincere thanks are extended to Mrs. Gladys Batson and Mrs. Peggy Denby for the heroic translation of our illegible manuscripts into the typed draft.

RANDOLPH W. CABELL
ALMARIN PHILLIPS

*Charlottesville*
*October, 1960*

# Contents

## APPENDIX

*problems in*
# BASIC OPERATIONS
# RESEARCH METHODS
*for management*

# part I Introduction

## 1 Introduction

### THE NATURE OF OPERATIONS RESEARCH

A well-known economist, pressed for a definition of his subject, opined somewhat facetiously that, "Economics is what economists do!" Whatever its shortcomings, this definition indicates the difficulty one has in communicating clearly and comprehensively the nature and scope of a particular branch of learning. Those working in a field—those who "do" it every day—acquire an almost intuitive grasp of what it is all about. Conveying this to others is not an easy task. This is especially true of operations research.

In the view of Churchman, Ackoff, and Arnoff, "O. R. in the most general sense can be characterized as the application of scientific methods, techniques, and tools to problems involving the operations of systems so as to provide those in control of the operations with optimum solutions to the problems." [1] Johnson says that, "In essence, operational research may be regarded as

---

[1] C. West Churchman, Russell L. Ackoff, and E. Leonard Arnoff, *Introduction to Operations Research,* John Wiley and Sons, New York, 1957, pp. 8–9.

1

the application of a theory of the reasoning process at all group levels from world wide and national down to that of the individual." [2] Or, again, he contends that O. R. "is the prediction and comparison of the values, effectiveness, and costs of a set of proposed alternative courses of action involving man-machine systems." [3] Many similar definitions have been attempted. Considered jointly, they suggest that O. R. may most easily be distinguished from other sciences and disciplines on the basis of a few outstanding characteristics.

First, O. R. has a broader scope than most other sciences and disciplines in two senses. Operations research adopts an organizational point of view. In a business, for example, O. R. looks at problems in terms of their relations to the business unit *as a whole* rather than in terms of suborganizations within the business. Production problems are interrelated with finance, marketing, and control. The solution of a problem in the production department in a manner optimal for that subgroup may create additional expense elsewhere. Operations research, taking the view of the entire organization, attempts to define such interrelationships and to solve problems in a way that is optimal in terms of the organization as a whole rather than "suboptimal" for a particular part of the organization.

In addition to the broad scope which results from the organizational point of view, O. R.'s breadth is further enlarged because of its applicability to any organization that has definable objectives, the attainment of which is subject to limitational contraints and pursuable by alternative means. The organization utilizing the O. R. method could be a business, an industry, the Department of Defense, a port authority, a hospital, or a city planning commission to mention but a few of the types of organizations which have, in fact, used the method.

Second, because of its breadth both within and among organizations, the O. R. method emphasizes the *development* of an analytic technique for solving individual problems rather than

2 Ellis A. Johnson, "The Long-Range Future of Operational Research," *Operations Research*, vol. 8, no. 1, January–February 1960.

3 Ellis A. Johnson, "The Executive, The Organization, and Operations Research," in *Operations Research for Management*, The Johns Hopkins Press, Baltimore, 1954, p. xxiii.

the *application* of generalized models. Organizations differ in size, complexity, objectives, and restraints. Although there may be many similarities between the problems confronting different organizations—more, in fact, than one would imagine—O. R. must be adaptive, flexible, and creative. In their detail, no two problems are precisely the same. Methods must be developed to fit the problem since, for the most part, it is fruitless to attempt to change a problem to fit existing methods of solution. Perhaps the most challenging aspect of O. R. is the development of models which are analogues of an organizational system. Operations research leans heavily on the basic sciences and mathematics in this respect. It cannot be restricted to these subjects, however, for the basic sciences and mathematics in their traditional forms have limitations in scope and method by which O. R., if it is to be successful, cannot be bound. The limitations of O. R. are imposed by the limits of man's reasoning ability, not by the content of specific disciplines.

These characteristics lead to a third. Obviously, an individual would be under great handicap were he to attempt fresh O. R. work by himself. It may often be possible for a person to apply and benefit from the use of particular tools and techniques which have arisen from previous basic O. R. work. But in dealing with new problems, with novel organizations, technologies, objectives, and restraints, a "team" effort is necessary. And the team, rather than being composed of persons with substantially similar backgrounds and interests, should bring together men from various disciplines and with different experiences. The breadth of many O. R. problems demands that, and, even in those instances when one person might learn to cope with the problem, the team approach often results in faster and more efficient methods of solution.

A fourth distinguishing characteristic of O. R. is that it is concerned with the practical management of an organization. The scientist working in O. R., John Lathrop asserts, "finds his problems in the harsh sunlight of the world of decision. He will retire with them to his world of science, to seek the underlying truths which make the operation tick. But he has not done his job until he comes forth again . . . and gives his answer to the impatient and fretting decision-maker, in the decision-maker's own language, in a form he can use at once." [4] In this respect, O. R. requires more than the use of the scientific method. It demands, in addition, positive conclusions and the communication of these conclusions to those whose function it is to decide and control. In performing this job, the scientist working in O. R. cannot ignore pure speculative research concerning the past and the future, but his most important function is with the present. Because of their decision-making orientation, O. R. models "implicitly or explicitly assume a penalty for delays." [5]

## THE TECHNIQUES OF OPERATIONS RESEARCH

The distinguishing characteristics of operations research provide at best only general insight into the nature of the subject. Operations research *is* what operations researchers do; closer inquiry into their occupation is necessary.

One distinguishing characteristic of O. R. noted above is its breadth of scope. Another is the development of models to fit particular problems. Viewed alone, it could be inferred from these characteristics that O. R. has not succeeded in producing any general models which may be applicable to broad classes of problems in an assortment of organizations. Such an inference would, however, be erroneous. Operations research, to a lesser extent, perhaps, than some of the more established and more specific sciences, has a small kit of techniques which are used quite widely. Some of them have been drawn from existing knowledge in allied fields. The nature of O. R., like that of the other sciences, can be better appreciated through an understanding of these techniques. It must be remembered, though, that these methods are products of *past* work in O. R. and the sciences on which O. R. has drawn. Although they are widely applicable and are finding increasing use in modern organizational management, a description of them suggests that the *research* aspect of O. R. is

[4] John B. Lathrop, "Operations Research Looks to Science," *Operations Research*, vol. 7, no. 4, July–August, 1959.

[5] C. West Churchman, "Why Measure," in *Measurement: Definitions and Theories*, Churchman and Ratoosh (eds.), John Wiley and Sons, New York, 1959, p. 93.

less important and the *applications* aspect more important than should be the case.

Allocation problems arise in virtually all organizations. They are problems concerning the optimum use of resources which are scarce relative to the activities in which they must be used. The problem is to allocate the resources among activities in an optimal way. Mathematical programming is one method commonly used in O. R. work in handling allocation problems. In general terms, mathematical programming involves algebraic statements of the objective function to be maximized (or minimized), of the alternative processes which may be used in attaining the objective, and of the restraints imposed by scarce resources and other factors, and then the use of matrix manipulations of the resulting systems of equations and inequations to achieve the maximum (minimum) possible value for the objective function.

At the present time, mathematical programming solutions to allocation problems are virtually limited to those in which objectives, restraints, and technical processes can be approximated by linear and homogeneous expressions. Certain nonlinear functions can be included by arbitrarily combining linear functions into approximations of convex or concave functions, and some progress has been made in incorporating second-degree functions. Beyond this, much remains to be done in generalizing nonlinear programming methods.

Mathematical programming may be applied to allocation problems which are dynamic—in the sense that some of the variables involved are functions of time—and to certain other problems in which uncertainty is involved and values appear as probability density functions rather than as parameters. In both of these cases, however, general methods are lacking and few practical problems lend themselves to solution because of difficulties of reliably identifying the relationships necessary for solution.

Another class of problems for which relatively general methods have been developed concerns the optimal control of inventories. A wide variety of organizations are characterized by a need for stocks of input and/or output materials because technical or economic reasons preclude simultaneous and identical flows into and out of the activities of the organization. Inventories are often susceptible to control which significantly affects the degree to which organizational goals are attained. Costs are usually associated with the size of inventory, with the frequency of orders or "set-ups" necessary to move materials either into or out of inventory, with shortages or inventory "stock-outs," and with changes in the rates of input and output flows. General inventory models exist which in many cases require little if any modification for optimal solutions to specific problems. When particular cases require a special solution, the models sometimes provide a convenient first approximation from which to progress.

Queuing, or "waiting-line," problems are also common to many organizational types. Queues result if units arrive for processing at a time when servicing facilities are not free to initiate processing immediately. Contrary to what at first seems intuitively obvious, the provision of service facilities adequate to service at a mean rate in excess of the mean arrival rate does not assure that no queue will arise. Instead, the relationship between the two rates defines (or helps to define) the expected length of the queue. Optimization requires the development of a model and of criteria for weighing the penalties of alternative queue lengths against the costs of alternative amounts of service facilities.

Sequencing (ordering) problems are related to queuing problems. In the latter, the central question is usually related to the amount of facilities to provide; in the former, it is to sequence and schedule jobs (arrivals) so that given facilities can be used ideally. Sequencing problems seem as ubiquitous as those dealing with allocation, inventory, and queues. They have not, however, proved as amenable to generalized models. For the most part, practical sequencing problems involve primary and original research in their solution.

Maintenance and replacement problems for facilities constitute another general class for which O. R. has developed fairly general approaches. When facilities consist of large numbers of items of the "one-horse shay" variety—performing with the same efficiency for a period of time and then failing completely—the models employed are fundamentally statistical in nature. Life expectancy of individual units of the population can be expressed as a function of time and a probability distribution of total failures (required replacements) generated. Additional information on the cost of replacing individual units as failure occurs, cost of replac-

ing in multiple units, and the penalties associated with not replacing immediately on failure usually leads to relatively simple
models for optimal replacement policies.

Optimal replacement policies for facilities which deteriorate
with age is somewhat more difficult, not because of complexity in
formulating a model but rather because of the paucity of relevant
information and inability to utilize probability functions to de-
scribe future uncertainties. As equipment ages its operating costs
may increase and the revenue derived from its productive services
may decrease. Since decisions to replace involve comparisons of
discounted future net proceeds for alternative equipment, "rule-
of-thumb" procedures based on untested assumptions concerning
the behavior of costs and revenue through time may be the best
available in practice.

Game theory and cybernetics have also offered models which
may properly be classified as O. R. techniques. Game theory involves competitive situations in which the objectives of two or
more "players" are in conflict in the sense that one becomes
"worse off" when another becomes "better off." Solution to a
game depends on the underlying rules governing conduct and the
choice of strategies employed by the players. Although few realistic and competitive management situations have as yet been
found which can profitably use the rather idealistic models of
game theory, some of the conclusions of the theory have been in-
directly useful in understanding the rationale and consequences
of particular management policies. Of special importance, perhaps, is that game theory has demonstrated that optimization is
a complex concept in problems involving interdependence and
conflict in the objectives of two or more persons (or organizations)
and that the application of the traditional calculus for maximization or minimization of objective functions in these cases is not
appropriate.

Cybernetics, the science of communication and control of organizational systems, has developed principally outside the pro-
fession of O. R. It is, nonetheless, an integral part of O. R. work
since the latter is dependent on effective communication and control.[6] Cybernetics, in fact, points to the most important reason

---

[6] Stafford Beer, *Cybernetics and Management,* John Wiley and Sons, New
York, 1959, pp. 182–183.

why O. R. applications have tended to be limited to relatively simple suboptimizing problems of management despite the broader objectives. Beer has noted that organizational management, in the cybernetic classificatory scheme, is an "activity which operates on the most advanced hypotheses about systems that are both complex and probabilistic. And it is at this point in the development of managerial technique," he continues, "that insuperable difficulties are reached. For . . . the company is in fact not merely complex, but exceedingly complex. . . . [We] are working with the unaided intelligence on problems of control which are manifestly too great for that intelligence." [7]

In addition to models or techniques that are applicable to certain types of problems, O. R. utilizes and has contributed to the development of general research methods. Some O. R. problems, either because they cannot be solved optimally with existing methods or because finding the optimal solution would be too laborious and time consuming, lend themselves to solution through a simulation of operation. Simulation, in the broad sense, consists of "operating" a model of an organizational system on a trial and error basis under differing decision rules. The best, or optimal, solution may not be found, and even if it is it probably remains unrecognized. Some operating rules, though, can be shown to produce "better" results than others. The existence of high-speed computers offers possibilities of finding in just a few hours the results of simulated operation analogous to several years of actual experience.

Simulation is not limited to particular types of problems. The Monte Carlo method of simulation, however, is especially useful for organizational problems in which several randomly behaving factors are interdependently involved in the outcome. For example, the management of a car rental agency wishes to determine the "best" size for its fleet of cars. Customers arrive at various mean rates during different hours of the day with specifiable variances about these means. Customers, once having rented cars, retain them for different times and drive different distances. Both the times and the distances can be expressed as frequency distributions. There are costs associated with outages and with keeping unrented cars. Revenues vary with both the time of the rental period and the miles driven. The problem is a real one and easy

7 *Ibid.*, pp. 132–133.

to conceptualize; it is not easy to solve in a formal way. A Monte Carlo solution would involve paper operation of the system under alternative fleet size conditions to determine which yields the highest contribution of those considered. With the aid of computers, quite reliable results can be obtained in a short time.

Statistics is an important tool in O. R. work. Constructing a model is one part of the job; obtaining data for implementation is quite another. The latter is an important function of statistical work. Beyond this, however, statistics has two other important contributions. One arises because of the common need for incorporating conditions of uncertainty in O. R. models. Mathematical statistics, through its facility in probability functions, is a direct aid in developing the appropriate model. The tools of statistical inference provide probability tests for an hypothesis which suggests the use of a particular probability function for a given set of data.

The second contribution of statistics beyond the provision of data is more intimately connected with organizational control. The results of many processes are affected by several random factors interacting with one another. The construction of a deterministic model to explain performance variance is impossible because of the fact of randomness. Yet process control may require an assignment of the total performance variance into component parts associated with the several factors involved in the process. The design of appropriate statistical experiments and the analysis of variance offer potentials for such problems which have hardly begun to be realized.

## OPERATIONS RESEARCH AND THE BUSINESS ADMINISTRATOR

Operations Research is an applied science directed toward "providing executive departments with a quantitative basis for decisions regarding the operations under their control." [8] It seems capable of contributing to substantial improvements in administration generally and, within the private sector of the economy, to business administration in particular.

[8] Philip M. Morse and George E. Kimball, *Methods of Operations Research*, John Wiley and Sons, New York, 1951, p. 1.

It has been noted that administrative problems within business are exceedingly complex. Many of the factors necessary to a decision are not quantifiable, even in an ordinal sense, by their very nature. Many are quantifiable conceptually but elude measurement. Some are so inextricably intertwined that decades may pass before a model of their organizational system can be created. As long as these conditions exist—and surely there is no foreseeable end to them—administrators will be forced to make decisions and exercise control in many areas without material aid from the scientific approach of O. R. There is, then, little likelihood that the O. R. team will make the conventional management team technologically obsolescent in the near future.

This is no reason for administrators to ignore operations research. Operations research has improved and will continue to improve administrative procedures if an effective channel of communication can be realized between the operational researcher and the professional administrator. In a passage cited above, Lathrop adopts the view that the burden of communication is on the O. R. man, that the O. R. man must give "his answer to the impatient and fretting decision-maker, in the decision-maker's own language, in a form he can use at once."

It is not clear that the burden of communication should be entirely on the O. R. worker. Neither is it obvious that the division of labor should be so complete that one whose principal work is in O. R. may not at the same time be one of the decision-makers nor that the decision-maker has no responsibility for learning something of "the world of science" to which the O. R. man retires for contemplation. If communication between the two is to be effective and if O. R. is to make its greatest contribution, each must know something of the other's job. Problems requiring solution come first to the attention of the administrator. Should he fail to recognize the problem or the possibility that O. R. may be helpful in its solution, much is lost. Operations research will never have a chance to help. Because of this it seems necessary that administrators know O. R. almost precisely in the sense the economist knew economics. The administrator ought to know O. R. in terms of what an O. R. team can and does do! The problems and exercises which follow, it is hoped, make a small contribution toward this end.

# part II Mathematical Programming Problems

## 2 Alpha Manufacturing Company
### *the transportation method*

The planned sales of the Alpha Manufacturing Company during the coming year were less than the company's capacity. The vice president in charge of production had assigned the bulk of the excess capacity to plant no. 1, leaving plant no. 2 to operate at near-full capacity and plant no. 3 to operate at full capacity. As a result of this, unit costs of production at plant no. 1 exceeded those at the other two plants. The plant manager of plant no. 1 reasoned that a more equal distribution of the excess capacity would tend to equalize the unit costs of production in the three plants and to increase the total company profits.

The Alpha Manufacturing Company produced a small component for an industrial product and distributed it to five wholesalers at a fixed delivered price of $2.50 per unit. Sales forecasts indicated that *monthly* deliveries to the five wholesalers during the next two quarters would be as shown in Exhibit I.

## EXHIBIT I

### MONTHLY DELIVERIES TO WHOLESALERS

| Wholesaler | Monthly Deliveries |
| --- | --- |
| No. 1 | 3,000 units |
| No. 2 | 3,000 units |
| No. 3 | 10,000 units |
| No. 4 | 5,000 units |
| No. 5 | 4,000 units |
| Total monthly deliveries | 25,000 units |

Alpha's three plants had the characteristics shown in Exhibit II.

## EXHIBIT II

### PLANT CHARACTERISTICS

| Plant Number | Production Capacity (units per Month) | Fixed (Overhead) Costs of Production per Month | Direct Costs of Production per Unit |
| --- | --- | --- | --- |
| 1 | 5,000 | $ 5,000 | $1.00 |
| 2 | 10,000 | 10,000 | 0.90 |
| 3 | 12,500 | 12,000 | 0.80 |

The five wholesalers were scattered through the sales territory of Alpha. Transportation costs from the various plants to the respective wholesalers are shown in Exhibit III.

Three thousand units of production per month had been assigned to plant no. 1, leaving 2000 units of excess capacity. Plant no. 2 was to produce 9500 units, with 500 units of excess capacity, and plant no. 3 was given 12,500 units of production, its full capacity. The manager of plant no. 1 figured his unit costs of production at $2.67 at this level of production, that is,

$$\frac{\$5000 + 3000\ (\$1.00)}{3000\ \text{units}}.$$

Plant no. 2, on the other hand, had unit costs of about $1.95 when operating at 9500 units per month, and plant no. 3 had unit costs of only $1.76 at capacity.

## EXHIBIT III

### TRANSPORTATION COSTS OF THE ALPHA COMPANY
### (IN DOLLARS PER UNIT)

| From Plant: | To Wholesaler: | | | | |
|---|---|---|---|---|---|
| | No. 1 | No. 2 | No. 3 | No. 4 | No. 5 |
| No. 1 | $0.05 | $0.07 | $0.10 | $0.15 | $0.15 |
| No. 2 | 0.08 | 0.06 | 0.09 | 0.12 | 0.14 |
| No. 3 | 0.10 | 0.09 | 0.08 | 0.10 | 0.15 |

The manager of plant no. 1 believed that this was an uneconomical production schedule and reasoned on the basis of spreading overhead costs. If plant no. 1 were to increase output by, say, 2000 units per month, the spreading of overhead would reduce costs in that plant to only $2.00 per unit, a reduction of $0.67 per unit. The same 2000 units, taken from plant no. 3, would increase unit costs there to only about $1.99, or by just $0.23 per unit. Thus he concluded there was a saving of $0.44 per unit ($0.67 − $0.23) in the transfer. Profits should rise by about $880.00 as a result (i. e., 2000 units times $0.44 per unit).

1. Express the profits of the Alpha Company in mathematical notation. (Let $X_1$, $X_2$, and $X_3$, represent the monthly production of plant nos. 1, 2, and 3, respectively. Let $x_{11}$, $x_{12}$, . . . , $x_{15}$ represent the deliveries *to* wholesalers 1, 2, . . . , 5 *by* plant no. 1, with similar nomenclature for plant nos. 2 and 3. Let $f_1$, $f_2$, and $f_3$ be the fixed costs of the respective plants. Let $d_1$, $d_2$, and $d_3$ be the direct costs per unit for the plants. Finally, let $c_{11}$, $c_{12}$, . . . , $c_{15}$ be the transportation costs from plant no. 1 to wholesalers 1, 2, . . . , 5, with similar nomenclature for the transportation costs from the other plants.)

2. Comment on the logic of the plant manager's argument.

3. Derive the optimal schedule with the transportation method. What is Alpha's profit (or loss) with this schedule? Be able to explain

verbally why this schedule is better from the standpoint of profit than any that would meet the plant manager's criterion.

# 3 Psi Metal-Working Company

*the "modi" method*

The Psi Company specialized in precision machining of metal parts from bar stock and casting blanks supplied by customers.

The production manager and the production control coordinator were discussing the work to be done in the turret lathe department for the next week in an effort to arrive at a schedule which would minimize costs or maximize profits. There were four orders to be produced for delivery by the end of the next week. (See Exhibit I.)

## EXHIBIT I

### ORDER QUANTITIES AND SELLING PRICES

| Order | Number of Pieces in Order | Price per Piece |
|-------|---------------------------|-----------------|
| 1 | 400 | $2.50 |
| 2 | 200 | 3.00 |
| 3 | 300 | 1.50 |
| 4 | 600 | 2.00 |

There were four machines available on which the orders could be produced. Three of these machines could be run only on a one-shift (forty-hour-per-week) basis, but the other machine could be run two shifts of forty hours each. The number of units of each order which could be produced on each machine are shown in Exhibit II. Machine B was one of the older machines and was not equipped to perform all the operations required by order 2.

## EXHIBIT II

### PRODUCTION RATES
### (PIECES PER HOUR)

| Machines | Orders | | | |
|---|---|---|---|---|
| | 1 | 2 | 3 | 4 |
| A | 7 | 6.3 | 5.6 | 8.4 |
| B | 8 | — | 6.4 | 9.6 |
| C | 10 | 9 | 8 | 12 |
| D | 7.5 | 6.75 | 6 | 9 |
| B with overtime | 8 | — | 6.4 | 9.6 |

The company maintained current records of operating costs per hour for each machine. These operating costs included direct labor and other variable costs. For specific jobs these costs were adjusted to take into account extra maintenance, lubrication, etc., caused by characteristics of the metal or the job. The adjusted hourly costs are the rates shown in Exhibit III.

## EXHIBIT III

### HOURLY COSTS FOR MACHINES AND ORDERS
### (DOLLARS PER OPERATING HOUR)

| Machines | Orders | | | |
|---|---|---|---|---|
| | 1 | 2 | 3 | 4 |
| A | 4.41 | 4.41 | 4.55 | 4.48 |
| B | 3.68 | — | 3.76 | 3.68 |
| C | 5.00 | 5.20 | 5.40 | 5.10 |
| D | 4.50 | 4.60 | 4.60 | 4.55 |
| B with overtime | 5.60 | — | 6.32 | 5.92 |

The production manager was aware of management's desire for profits; yet, he also was responsible for keeping costs to a minimum in his department. He was not quite sure how to approach the scheduling problem, since he was not sure that a minimum-cost program to meet the orders would be a maximum-profit program.

1. Using the "modi" method, determine the optimum program (either minimum cost or maximum profits) which you believe should be used.
2. Would your reasoning and conclusions on cost minimization versus profit maximization be the same if order 3 were for *at least* 300 pieces?

# 4 Beta Machine Products Company

*the simplex method*

The Beta Machine Products Company was faced with the problem of scheduling production and subcontracting for three products. The products were sold to larger industrial firms at fixed f.o.b. contract prices, and Beta was anxious to supply the product or products in the quantities that would be most profitable.

Each of the products required casting, machining, and assembly and packaging. Castings operations for products 1 and 2 could be subcontracted, but the castings for product 3 required special equipment which precluded the use of subcontractors. Direct costs of the three operations, the prices for the products, and the respective contributions to overhead and profits are shown in Exhibit I.

Each unit of product 1 required six minutes of casting time (if done at Beta), six minutes of machining time, and three minutes for assembly and packaging. For product 2, the times were ten minutes, three minutes, and two minutes, respectively. A unit of product 3 took eight minutes for casting, eight minutes for machining, and two minutes for assembly and packaging.

Beta had capacities of 8000 minutes of casting time, 12,000 minutes of machining time, and 10,000 minutes of assembly and packaging time per week.

## EXHIBIT I

## DIRECT COSTS, PRICES, AND CONTRIBUTIONS TO OVERHEAD AND PROFITS

| Item | Product 1 | Product 2 | Product 3 |
|---|---|---|---|
| Cost of castings: | | | |
| Produced at Beta | $0.30 | $0.50 | $0.40 |
| Subcontracted | .50 | .60 | — |
| Cost of machining | .20 | .10 | .27 |
| Cost of assembly and packaging | .30 | .20 | .20 |
| Price | 1.50 | 1.80 | 1.97 |
| Contribution to overhead and profit: | | | |
| With castings produced at Beta | .70 | 1.00 | 1.10 |
| With casting subcontracted | .50 | .90 | — |

1. Express the objective function to be maximized mathematically.
2. Express the constraining inequations mathematically.
3. Solve the problem by the simplex method. Check each step to see whether your solution is tending toward optimal profits. Check each step to see whether the constraining conditions are being violated.
4. Be able to explain in words the reasons the scheduled solution is preferable to any other.

# 5 Lambda Fertilizer Company

## *the simplex method*

The Lambda Fertilizer Company will have available to it in the coming month 1000 tons of nitrates, 1800 tons of phosphates, and 1200 tons of potash. These quantities are on hand or have already been ordered, and no more can be received until after the next thirty days have passed. The firm is interested in mixing these active ingredients together with certain inert ingredients,

which are available in unlimited supply, into three basic fertilizer
mixes in whatever way will maximize profits in the coming month.

The three basic fertilizers are 5–10–5, 5–10–10, and 10–10–10,
the numbers representing in each case the percentage (by weight)
of nitrates, phosphates, and potash, respectively, in each of the
mixes.

Costs of the fertilizer ingredients are shown in Exhibit I. Costs
of mixing, packaging, and selling are identical for all three mixes
and amount to $15 per ton.

### EXHIBIT I

#### COST OF FERTILIZER INGREDIENTS
#### (PER TON)

| | |
|---|---|
| Nitrates | $160 |
| Phosphates | 40 |
| Potash | 100 |
| Inert ingredients | 5 |

Prices for the mixed fertilizer are set competitively, and the
Lambda Company cannot control them. At present these prices
are as shown in Exhibit II. All fertilizer produced can be sold at
these prices, but there is a sales commitment to deliver 6000 tons
of 5–10–5 within the month.

### EXHIBIT II

#### PRICES OF MIXED FERTILIZERS
#### (PER TON)

| | |
|---|---|
| 5–10–5 | $40 |
| 5–10–10 | 50 |
| 10–10–10 | 60 |

1. How much fertilizer of each type should be produced this month?

# 6 The Southern Cotton Mill *

## the simplex method

The Southern Cotton Mill produced cotton cloth in several styles. The production process, which employed about 200 people and operated on three shifts of forty hours each, involved carding, drawing, spinning, and weaving operations. The mill was interested in determining the most profitable mix of styles for the coming season.

The Sales Department had selected eight styles for production. Prices had been set for each style which assured the mill that it could sell all of each style it produced. The contribution to profit and overhead for the style at these prices is shown in Exhibit I.

### EXHIBIT I

### CONTRIBUTION TO PROFIT AND OVERHEAD FOR EIGHT STYLES (IN DOLLARS PER 100,000 YARDS)

| Style | Contribution |
|-------|--------------|
| A | $400 |
| B | 370 |
| C | 360 |
| D | 360 |
| E | 350 |
| F | 330 |
| G | 280 |
| H | 275 |

Each style required production time on all four of the processes. Total available time is given in Exhibit II. The production hours required for each style in each process is given in Exhibit III.

---

* This problem was prepared and solved by N. L. Enrick, Director of Operations Research, Institute of Textile Technology, Charlottesville, Virginia. It is reproduced with the express permission of Mr. Enrick and the Institute of Textile Technology.

## EXHIBIT II

### AVAILABLE PROCESS TIME PER 120 HOUR WEEK (IN THOUSANDS OF HOURS)

| Process | Available Time |
|---------|----------------|
| Carding | 26.0 |
| Drawing | 242.0 |
| Spinning | 7,200.0 |
| Weaving | 250.0 |

## EXHIBIT III

### THOUSANDS OF PRODUCTION HOURS PER HUNDRED THOUSAND YARDS

| Style | Carding | Drawing | Spinning | Weaving |
|-------|---------|---------|----------|---------|
| A | 1.8 | 36.0 | 720.0 | 30.6 |
| B | 2.6 | 28.8 | 648.0 | 30.6 |
| C | 2.4 | 28.8 | 720.0 | 32.6 |
| D | 2.1 | 28.8 | 648.0 | 30.6 |
| E | 2.9 | 31.2 | 648.0 | 26.5 |
| F | 2.1 | 36.0 | 720.0 | 30.6 |
| G | 2.9 | 21.6 | 792.0 | 22.4 |
| H | 2.9 | 36.0 | 720.0 | 32.8 |

1. What style mix yields the maximum total contribution to profits and overhead?

# 7 Kappa Manufacturing Company
*convex programming and the simplex method*

The production manager of the Kappa Manufacturing Company was given a rush order for quantities of three different products, A, B, and C. Since the order came from one of Kappa's good customers, management wished to get the order out within one week.

The three products had all been manufactured by Kappa so drawings and standards were available. Kappa also had sufficient material and components for the products.

The company was operating a day shift and a night shift but was not utilizing the full two-shift capacity at this time. This excess time plus time made available by rescheduling other jobs made time available to produce the A, B, and C units as indicated in Exhibit I.

### EXHIBIT I

### AVAILABLE TIME
### (IN HOURS)

|  | Day Shift | Night Shift |
|---|---|---|
| Stamping and welding | 30 | 35 |
| Subassembly | 25 | 30 |
| Final assembly and packing | 40 | 35 |

It was a policy of the company not to transfer units between shifts. That is, a unit which had been through stamping and welding on the day shift must go to the other two departments on the day shift. It could not go to either of the departments on the night shift.

Productivity varied between the two shifts as is shown in Exhibit II.

Likewise, the direct costs of labor and overhead per unit out-

## EXHIBIT II

### PRODUCTIVITY PER SHIFT
### (UNITS PER HOUR)

| Department | Day Shift | | | Night Shift | | |
|---|---|---|---|---|---|---|
| | A | B | C | A | B | C |
| Stamping and welding | 5 | 3 | 5 | 3 | 2 | 3 |
| Subassembly | 6 | 4 | 4 | 5 | 2 | 2 |
| Final assembly and packing | 4 | 3 | 2 | 4 | 3 | 2 |

put varied between shifts. The direct labor, material and over-head costs are summarized in Exhibit III.

### EXHIBIT III

#### COSTS PER UNIT

| Product | Day Shift | Night Shift |
|---|---|---|
| A | $11 | $16 |
| B | 10 | 14 |
| C | 12 | 18 |

The customer needed exactly sixty units of A and forty units of C. He needed at least sixty units of B but would take more than this. The contracted prices to the customer are shown in Exhibit IV.

### EXHIBIT IV

#### SELLING PRICES OF PRODUCTS

| Product | Price |
|---|---|
| A | $25 |
| B | 15 |
| C | 20 |

1. Develop a program using the simplex method which will maximize profits on the contract.

2. What considerations regarding costs and scheduling are important but are not brought out in the case?

# 8 Taylor and Lockhart Farms *

*programming with more complicated restraints*

Mr. Joe Taylor and Mr. John Lockhart were interested in devising a plan that would enable them to maximize the total contribution to fixed overhead and profits from their farms. Recently enacted Federal legislation affected their operations and required them to devise new methods for using their land.

Prior to Federal acreage restrictions these two producers considered cotton their primary crop and planted all of their acreage in cotton. However, because of the new cotton acreage restrictions, maize, tomatoes, and cabbage and the Conservation Reserve Program have to be considered as alternate ways of utilizing all of their tillable acreage (see Exhibit I).

### EXHIBIT I

#### ACREAGE AVAILABLE

| | Taylor | | | Lockhart | | |
|---|---|---|---|---|---|---|
| | | Cotton | | | Cotton | |
| Type Farm | Total | Plan A | Plan B | Total | Plan A | Plan B |
| Rented irrigated | 21.8 | 17.2 | 21.3 | 40.0 | 17.6 | 24.6 |
| Own irrigated | 558.0 | 233.8 | 327.3 | — | — | — |
| Rented dry | — | — | — | 1772.9 | 1098.7 | 1538.7 |
| Own dry | 580.0 | 223.9 | 313.5 | 806.0 | 323.7 | 453.2 |

* This case was prepared by Mr. Spencer Buchanan.

## COTTON

The legislation set forth two plans between which Mr. Taylor and Mr. Lockhart had to choose in deciding how much acreage to devote to cotton. Plan A provided for a support level of 80 per cent of parity and an acreage allotment identical to that of the previous year. Plan B allowed a 40 per cent increase in the acreage allotment but reduced the support level to 65 per cent of parity. Thus, depending on the contribution from each farm, the total contribution from cotton was affected by the choice of plans.

Because of the governmental surplus of cotton, the two farmers felt that a conservative approach required that the cotton contribution be based on the support price. Actual market prices in the past had remained fairly close to the support price. Previous records provided very accurate information on yields, and these growers expected future yields to remain near the same level (see Exhibits II and III).

### EXHIBIT II

#### YIELDS PER ACRE FOR THE SEVERAL CROPS

|  | Taylor | | Lockhart | |
| --- | --- | --- | --- | --- |
|  | Dry Land | Irrigated | Dry Land | Irrigated |
| Cotton (bales) | .8 | 1.6 | .8 | 1.2 |
| Maize (cwt) | 30 | 40 | 27 | 16 |
| Tomatoes (1000 lb) | 2 | 3 | 2 | 3 |
| Cabbage (ton) | 6 | 8 | 6 | 8 |

Based on the assurance of the support price and the yield from cotton, the growers wanted to plant as much cotton as possible under whichever plan they chose. One reason for this was that, even though the marketing process for cotton is somewhat involved, cash is realized shortly after harvest (see Exhibit IV). Another point considered was that each type of land on each farm could be placed independently in either plan A or plan B.

EXHIBIT III

## CONTRIBUTION PER CROP UNIT FOR VARIOUS CROPS ON DIFFERENT LANDS

| | Taylor | | | Lockhart | | |
|---|---|---|---|---|---|---|
| | Rented | Owned | | Rented | | Owned |
| | Irrigated | Irrigated | Dry | Irrigated | Dry | Dry |
| Cotton plan A | $ 81.00 | $130.00 | $124.00 | $ 62.00 | $ 76.00 | $126.00 |
| Cotton plan B | 53.00 | 101.00 | 95.00 | 45.00 | 46.00 | 97.00 |
| Maize | .45 | .96 | .90 | .00 | .55 | 1.03 |
| Tomatoes: high | 300.00 | 300.00 | 200.00 | 300.00 | 200.00 | 200.00 |
| average | 22.50 | 31.50 | 26.00 | 22.50 | 16.60 | 26.00 |
| low * | (11.80) | (11.80) | (11.60) | (11.80) | (11.60) | (11.60) |
| Cabbage: high | 12.00 | 22.00 | 24.00 | 12.00 | 12.00 | 24.00 |
| average | 5.70 | 11.20 | 11.90 | 5.70 | 6.00 | 11.90 |
| low * | (8.80) | (8.80) | (8.10) | (8.80) | (8.10) | (8.10) |

The Conservation Reserve Program would contribute $20.00 per acre per year for all types of owned land and $16.00 per acre per year for all types of rented land.

* Parentheses indicate negative amounts.

EXHIBIT IV

## PLANTING DATES AND HARVESTING DATES

| | Planting Date | Harvesting Date |
|---|---|---|
| Cotton | 1 February | 1 July |
| Maize | 1 March | 15 June |
| Tomatoes | 15 March | 15 June |
| Cabbage | 15 September | 15 December |

## MAIZE

No Federal legislation limited the amount of maize that could be planted. Maize is supported by government loans, however, and Mr. Taylor and Mr. Lockhart could count on an assured market for all their maize at a specified price prior to planting. Although the contribution from maize was low relative to cotton (see Exhibit III), it was an easy crop to produce and was harvested before cotton, thereby providing an opportunity to utilize machinery and labor which would otherwise be idle.

In order to be conservative, the two farmers based the contribution from maize on the maize support price. Also, since maize has an easy marketing process, the growers were assured of cash shortly after harvest.

## TOMATOES

Tomato prices were not supported by the government and were a risky crop to grow because of market price fluctuations. Mr. Taylor and Mr. Lockhart were interested only in a plan that would assure at least no over-all loss even if the price of tomatoes were to drop to the lowest levels conceivable.

## CABBAGE

Cabbage, like tomatoes, was not supported by the government and was also a risky crop from a market standpoint. Although losses were possible because of changes in markets, the crop is appealing because it is grown after all other crops have been harvested. However, Mr. Taylor and Mr. Lockhart were interested in planting cabbage only to the point that no over-all loss could possibly be incurred.

## CONSERVATION RESERVE PROGRAM

Mr. Taylor and Mr. Lockhart were also studying a Conservation Reserve Program that would retire part of their land from production for five years. The land placed in the program could not be devoted to the production of any crops but would not affect their cotton acreage. A limit of $5000 in annual rentals per individual restricted the amount of land that could be placed in this program.

# 9 Sierra Mills, Incorporated

*programming under uncertain conditions*

Sierra Mills was a medium-sized textile firm located in the southern part of the country. Although they sold a large number of different fabrics, two basic types accounted for over 90 per cent of the sales volume.

The two types of products went through the same three-stage manufacturing process. However, because each type had different weave and finish requirements, different times were required by each fabric in these three stages or departments. The processing times for fabrics and departments are shown in Exhibit I. The

### EXHIBIT I

PROCESSING TIMES OF FABRICS IN EACH DEPARTMENT
(IN MINUTES PER THOUSAND YARDS)

| Fabric | Departments | | |
|---|---|---|---|
| | A | B | C |
| 1 | 12.0 | 14.4 | 15.0 |
| 2 | 18.0 | 16.6 | 13.7 |

company worked three shifts, five days a week, fifty weeks a year.

Toward the end of each fiscal year, the company estimated the sales of its fabrics for the following year. Materials were procured, and production was scheduled on the basis of these estimates. This schedule could be changed during the year, but, because of a long lead time for materials and because of high set-up costs, the company tried to keep the number of changes to a minimum.

Recently the company had begun planning with profit maximization for the year as the primary objective. This entailed the choice of what fabrics to produce in order to realize maximum profit. It also placed great emphasis on accurate sales estimates, but experience had shown that sales were rarely within 20 per cent of the estimates. In an attempt to overcome this difficulty, management decided for the next year to include in its sales estimates the chance or probability of sales exceeding certain figures. Accordingly, estimates were made for the two products at three levels of probability. These are given in Exhibit II. For

### EXHIBIT II

### SALES ESTIMATES
### (IN MILLIONS OF YARDS)

| Fabric | Probability of Sales | | |
|:---:|:---:|:---:|:---:|
|  | 0.70 | 0.50 | 0.30 |
| 1 | 9 | 12 | 15 |
| 2 | 12 | 15 | 18 |

example, management estimated that there was only a 30 per cent chance that 15 million yards or more of fabric 1 would be sold during the next year. They felt that there was a 70 per cent chance that 9 million yards or more would be sold.

Each 1000 yards of fabric 1 which was sold contributed $40 to fixed costs and profit, and each 1000 yards of fabric 2 contributed $50.

1. Determine the product mix which will lead to maximum profits on the basis of the information management has available at this time.

# 10 Gamma Valve Company

*Flood's assignment method*

An operator on the assembly line of the Gamma Valve Company, manufacturers of precision valves, had the job of inserting a metal ball in valve assemblies. As an assembly came to her, she measured the inside diameter of the valve and inserted a ball of proper diameter.

A box with eight small bins was placed directly in front of the operator. The bins were designed to hold the eight size groups into which the balls had been sorted. Since much of the operators' work consisted of reaching into the bins for the proper ball, the efficiency of her work would be increased by minimizing the amount of reaching she had to do.

The eight bins involved reaches as shown in Exhibit I.

### EXHIBIT I

#### INCHES OF REACH TO BINS

| Bin No. | Inches of Reach |
|:---:|:---:|
| 1 | 7 |
| 2 | 8 |
| 3 | 9 |
| 4 | 8 |
| 5 | 10 |
| 6 | 11 |
| 7 | 12 |
| 8 | 11 |

The balls varied from uniform diameter because of machining, grinding, and polishing variations. The internal diameter of the valve assemblies varied for similar reasons. The operators' job was to match valves with slightly larger-than-specified diameters with balls slightly in excess of specifications (and vice versa).

A study of variances from specifications showed that, on the average, the number of balls of various diameters used for each 100 assemblies was distributed as shown in Exhibit II.

EXHIBIT II

| Ball Group | Range of Ball Diameters | Average Number Used per Hundred Assemblies |
|:---:|:---:|:---:|
| 1 | 4.9960–4.9969 | 3 |
| 2 | 4.9970–4.9979 | 10 |
| 3 | 4.9980–4.9989 | 15 |
| 4 | 4.9990–4.9999 | 25 |
| 5 | 5.0000–5.0009 | 30 |
| 6 | 5.0010–5.0019 | 10 |
| 7 | 5.0020–5.0029 | 5 |
| 8 | 5.0030–5.0039 | 2 |
| | | 100 |

1. Use Flood's technique for solving the assignment problem to determine in which bin each of the groups of balls should be placed so as to minimize the amount of reaching done by the operator.

# 11 Omicron Airfreight Company

*Flood's assignment method*

The Omicron Airfreight Company was a nonscheduled airline which picked up and delivered freight where the customers required. The company operated several types of cargo aircraft, but all could be grouped into either post-World War II or pre-World War II aircraft, X and Y, respectively. The two categories had essentially the same load capabilities, but the newer aircraft were cheaper to operate. All variable costs, such as fuel, oil and servicing, etc., are shown in Exhibit I.

On a particular day, the dispatcher at Omicron's headquarters

## EXHIBIT I

### SUMMARY OF OPERATING COSTS

| | Cost per Mile | |
|---|---|---|
| Type of Aircraft | Empty | Loaded |
| X | $1.00 | $2.00 |
| Y | 1.50 | 3.00 |

was faced with the problem of scheduling the pick-up and delivery of loads for six customers.

There were six aircraft available for the jobs. The type of aircraft and their locations are shown in Exhibit II.

## EXHIBIT II

### DISTRIBUTION OF AVAILABLE AIRCRAFT

| Location | Type of Aircraft |
|---|---|
| J | X |
| K | Y |
| L | Y |
| M | X |
| N | Y |
| P | X |

Each of the six customers had about the same size of load, and all loads required the same amount of handling, packing, etc. The distance in miles between the loading points and the final destinations for the six customers are shown in Exhibit III.

The distances between the present location of aircraft and the loading points (in miles) are given in Exhibit IV.

The dispatcher wished to minimize the total cost of the six complete trips which were required by the schedule. (One complete trip is defined as moving an aircraft from its present location to the loading point where it picks up freight, and from there to the final destination.)

EXHIBIT III

DISTANCES BETWEEN LOADING POINTS AND
FINAL DESTINATIONS

| | |
|---|---|
| A–a | 600 |
| B–b | 300 |
| C–c | 1000 |
| D–d | 500 |
| E–e | 400 |
| F–f | 200 |

EXHIBIT IV

DISTANCES BETWEEN PRESENT LOCATION OF
AIRCRAFT AND LOADING POINTS

| Present Location of Aircraft | Loading Points | | | | | |
|---|---|---|---|---|---|---|
| | A | B | C | D | E | F |
| J | 300 | 200 | 400 | 100 | 200 | 200 |
| K | 300 | 100 | 300 | 200 | 500 | 400 |
| L | 400 | 100 | 100 | 500 | 100 | 100 |
| M | 200 | 200 | 400 | 200 | 300 | 500 |
| N | 300 | 200 | 100 | 300 | 400 | 400 |
| P | 200 | 100 | 200 | 400 | 400 | 200 |

1. Determine the allocation which minimizes total cost.
2. What is the total cost under the allocation found in question 1?

# 12 Delta Machine Tool Department

*short-cut and approximation methods*

The machine tool department of the Delta Company was a bottleneck to the company's production capacity. The department had five basic types of machine tools and worked two forty-hour-per-week shifts. The number of machines of each type is shown in Exhibit I. Types D and E were older machines and generally less efficient in operation.

## EXHIBIT I

### NUMBER OF MACHINE TOOLS

| Type | Number |
|------|--------|
| A | 12 |
| B | 8 |
| C | 15 |
| D | 6 |
| E | 2 |

The machine tool department was scheduled to run six separate jobs in a coming week. From previous experience with the specifi-

## EXHIBIT II

### HOURS OF MACHINE TIME PER UNIT

| Machine Type | Job | | | | | |
|------|---|---|---|---|---|---|
| | 1 | 2 | 3 | 4 | 5 | 6 |
| A | 10 | 3 | 15 | 3 | 5 | 6 |
| B | 12 | 2 | 20 | 2 | 6 | 5 |
| C | 8 | 4 | 22 | 3 | 7 | 4 |
| D | 9 | 6 | 16 | 6 | 8 | 7 |
| E | 15 | 5 | 20 | 6 | 10 | 8 |

cations of these jobs and time studies done to establish piece rates for the operators, the number of hours required on each type of machine for a unit of each of the jobs was known. They are shown in Exhibit II.

Exhibit III gives the number of units involved in each job. Since the department had proven to be a bottleneck, the assignment of jobs to machines had to be done in a way which would use as little total machine time as possible.

### EXHIBIT III

#### NUMBER OF UNITS REQUIRED

| Job | Number of Units |
| --- | --- |
| 1 | 100 |
| 2 | 150 |
| 3 | 40 |
| 4 | 50 |
| 5 | 100 |
| 6 | 200 |

# part III Inventory Problems

## 13 Bravo Manufacturing Company
*constant demand*

The plant manager of the Bravo Manufacturing Company had been assigned the production of 2500 units of production per month and the delivery of these units to one customer. Factors beyond his control made it necessary to produce the 2500 units at an even rate throughout the month. He was now confronted with the problem of deciding the quantities in which these 2500 units should be delivered.

He had calculated previously that transportation costs from the plant to the customer amounted to $0.05 per unit. The plant operated its own truck and had been accustomed to delivering 1000 units at a time. Each shipment involved costs of $40 regardless of the number of units shipped. This amount covered gas and oil and certain other cost elements which did not vary appreciably with the size of the load. In addition, it had been estimated that the expenses of loading and unloading, etc., cost $0.01 per unit. The customary load of 1000 units cost $40 plus 1000 times $0.01, a total of $50. Thus the full cost per unit in such a shipment was $0.05.

The trucks were capable of handling loads up to 2500 units. The manager reasoned that it might be more economical to let the inventory of finished products build up to 2500 before shipping. By so doing, delivery costs per shipment would be $40 plus 2500 times $0.01, or $65. On this basis, the delivery costs per unit would fall to $0.0267, slightly more than one-half of what they were with delivery lots of 1000.

The plant manager hesitated before making this decision. The higher average inventory that the decision involved troubled him. Bravo was borrowing money at 6 per cent at the time and using it to expand facilities, the return from which was estimated at 24 per cent per year. And it seemed clear that every unit of production in inventory at the plant was tying up capital. The out-of-pocket costs of production were $1.00 per unit so that inventory was worth at least this amount. Viewed in another way, each time the customer received a shipment, Bravo received $2.50 per unit in return.

# 14 Lynchburg Foundry Company*

*uncertain demand*

In October 1958, Mr. E. F. Pierce, Manager of the Methods Department of the Lynchburg Foundry Company, was checking the records of cut-off wheels used by the company in its ductile iron work. Increased ductile iron production in the past twelve months had required a corresponding increase in the use of cut-off wheels and a more than proportional increase in the average level of stocks of wheels. Since the trend in ductile iron was expected to continue, Mr. Pierce was interested in establishing a policy that would control the chance of being out of wheels when they were needed but that at the same time would not re-

* This case is reproduced with the express permission of the Lynchburg Foundry Company, Lynchburg, Virginia.

quire an excessive amount of inventory of wheels to be carried.

The Lynchburg Foundry Company had two plants in southwestern Virginia, and it employed over 1000 workers. The company was founded in the 1890's to produce agricultural implements and parts for agricultural machinery. It expanded rapidly in this field and in 1906 added equipment to produce cast-iron pipe. Over the next fifty years, the company diversified further into military and industrial markets. The company management placed great emphasis on research and development, and this policy, through the years, resulted in many advantages for the company in the fields of metallurgy and foundry practice.

Until 1949 most of the output of the foundry in Lynchburg had been gray iron castings. In that year, however, the company was licensed by the International Nickel Company to produce ductile iron, and an experimental program was undertaken which would lead eventually to large-scale production of ductile iron. Ductile iron is produced by chemically treating iron in its molten state to give it greater strength and ductility. The main advantage of ductile iron over gray iron is that ductile iron is not as brittle as gray iron and, hence, cannot be broken as easily as gray iron. Most of the production processes for the two types of iron are similar; however, some changes are necessary in the steps following the casting of the ductile iron.

In producing a casting, provisions must be made for the introduction of molten metal into the mold and for flow of molten metal into spaces created by the cooling, contracting metal in the castings. To meet these requirements, channels and spaces are provided in the mold to supply molten metal to the casting itself. After cooling, the metal in these spaces remains attached to the casting and must be removed. The complete casting is removed from the mold, and these "gates and risers" (as they are called) usually are knocked off the gray iron castings by a blow of some kind, and the remaining small protrusions are removed with a grinding wheel. For ductile iron, however, because of the quality of the iron and the large weight of gates and risers in relation to the casting itself, a blow will not separate the gates and risers. Consequently, most of the gates and risers must be cut off by machine. The cutting is done with a high-speed, motor-driven rotary wheel which "saws" through the gates and risers. The wheels are between 7 inches and 20 inches in diameter, 3/8 inch thick, and made of an abrasive-impregnated fiber material. Wear on the wheel is quite rapid. Cutting operations on twenty-five castings may wear as much as 4 inches off the diameter of the wheel. Wear rate for each casting depends primarily on the number and size of gates and risers.

The ductile iron castings produced in the foundry vary in size and shape so that it is necessary to have at least 16-inch-diameter wheels to reach the gates and risers on some castings, while wheels as small as 7 inches in diameter can be used on others. Wheels of less than 7-inch diameter are useless. The company can purchase wheels of three sizes—20, 16, and 10 inches—to use on their machines. They have one cutting machine capable of using 20-inch wheels, an additional machine capable of using 16-inch wheels, and several portable machines on which 10-inch wheels can be mounted.

As ductile iron assumed more prominence in the company's operations, attempts were made to utilize fully each wheel. The majority of castings can be cut off with either a 16- or 20-inch wheel. When a high production of ductile iron is undertaken, both the 16- and 20-inch machines are used on the same type of casting. The company has developed a policy of purchasing only 20-inch wheels, and as they are worn down, to remove them from the 20-inch machine and pass them down to the 16-inch machine. After the wheels have worn to 12 or 13 inches, they are transferred to the 10-inch machines where they are used until the diameter is ground down to 7 inches, at which time the wheels are discarded. Following this policy, there should never be an excess of 16-inch wheels. The 10-inch wheels are not used as rapidly as the 16- and 20-inch wheels; hence, a surplus might appear over a period of time. There is no salvage value for the wheels at any time after they have been used. Wheels are checked out of the storeroom where records of inventory are kept. Notation is made when the wheels are checked out, by the order clerk. When the inventory drops to twenty-five or thirty wheels, the clerk initiates an order for 100 wheels. Wheels usually are received between three days and one week from the date the order is initiated. If a large run of ductile iron is expected, the re-order point is adjusted upward from twenty-five or thirty wheels. Wheels are received in packages of about seventeen wheels each. Some packages, however, might have only fifteen, and others could have as many as nineteen.

To assist him in coming to some conclusion about the cut-off wheels, Mr. Pierce had assembled the following records:

Record of orders for 20-inch wheels (Exhibit I)
Check-out of 20-inch wheels (Exhibit II)

### EXHIBIT I

### RECORD OF ORDERS FOR 20-INCH WHEELS

| Date Received | Size of Order | Value of Order | Inventory after Receipt of Order |
|---|---|---|---|
| 1957 27 Aug. | 71 | $ 951 | 96 |
| 12 Sept. | 21 | 281 | 36 |
| 13 Sept. | 125 | 1675 | 161 |
| 30 Oct. | 20 | 268 | 20 |
| 1 Nov. | 50 | 670 | 55 |
| 25 Nov. | 58 | 777 | 59 |
| 26 Nov. | 50 | 670 | 50 |
| 5 Dec. | 51 | 683 | 51 |
| 16 Dec. | 40 | 536 | 40 |
| 23 Dec. | 44 | 589 | 44 |
| 1958 8 Jan. | 42 | 563 | 49 |
| 20 Jan. | 54 | 724 | 54 |
| 29 Jan. | 44 | 590 | 74 |
| 3 Feb. | 49 | 657 | 111 |
| 10 Feb. | 54 | 724 | 151 |
| 18 Feb. | 47 | 630 | 167 |
| 3 Mar. | 91 | 1219 | 202 |
| 21 Mar. | 56 | 750 | 227 |
| 31 Mar. | 44 | 589 | 263 |
| 21 Apr. | 55 | 563 | 231 |
| 4 June | 103 | 1055 | 169 |
| 16 July | 107 | 1096 | 179 |
| 22 Aug. | 101 | 1034 | 102 |
| 15 Sept. | 101 | 1034 | 101 |
| 29 Sept. | 103 | 1055 | 146 |

## EXHIBIT II

### CHECK-OUT OF 20-INCH WHEELS

| Date | Number of Wheels Checked Out | Date | Number of Wheels Checked Out |
|------|------------------------------|------|------------------------------|
| 1958 21 May | 7 | 11 Aug. | 20 |
| 22 | 12 | 12 | 17 |
| 23 | 7 | 13 | 2 |
| 3 June | 2 | 13 | 2 |
| 4 | 8 | 14 | 15 |
| 5 | 6 | 15 | 1 |
| 5 | 8 | 19 | 5 |
| 10 | 8 | 22 | 33 |
| 12 | 6 | 25 | 3 |
| 13 | 8 | 26 | 4 |
| 16 | 14 | 28 | 3 |
| 17 | 2 | 29 | 20 |
| 18 | 3 | 2 Sept. | 6 |
| 19 | 12 | 3 | 20 |
| 20 | 6 | 8 | 4 |
| 24 | 5 | 8 | 4 |
| 25 | 11 | 11 | 7 |
| VACATION | | 15 | 2 |
| 17 Jul. | 10 | 16 | 18 |
| 18 | 6 | 17 | 16 |
| 21 | 6 | 18 | 14 |
| 24 | 6 | 24 | 6 |
| 25 | 12 | 29 | 4 |
| 28 | 12 | 2 Oct. | 7 |
| 29 | 15 | 3 | 6 |
| 30 | 15 | 6 | 10 |
| 31 | 6 | 8 | 2 |
| 1 Aug. | 6 | 9 | 4 |
| 7 | 6 | | |
| 8 | 18 | | |

In addition to these records, Mr. Pierce had gathered some information concerning costs within the company. He knew that insurance rates for merchandise in the company warehouse were $0.34 per $100 value per year. Since the wheels were compactly packaged and required little space in the warehouse, he did not believe there were any additional storage costs. No survey had been made recently in the company to determine the cost of processing orders, but he estimated that it cost about $1.00 for each order and that this would be the same regardless of the size of the order. This cost included the initial order and handling after receipt of the order. He was aware that for the past several years, the company had earned around 20 per cent before taxes on money invested internally.

On the basis of the information available, Mr. Pierce wondered if he could arrive at the answers to the following questions:

1. If operations and costs in 1959 are at the same level as they have been for the past twelve months, what is the optimum quantity which should be ordered each time? What will be the number of orders placed in 1959? What will be the total cost?
2. What would be the effect on the optimum re-order quantity and the costs related to cut-off wheels, if the actual use of cut-off wheels were double the estimated use?
3. If management is willing to accept a 5 per cent risk in maintaining an inventory of cut-off wheels, what should the re-order point, or safety stock, be?

# 15 Epsilon Office Supply Company

*uncertain demand and outage costs*

The Epsilon Office Supply Company sold typewriters, adding machines, desk calculators, duplicating equipment, paper, ink, etc. In addition to these items for businesses, it also carried a line of portable typewriters. Sales of the portables accounted for an appreciable portion of Epsilon's total sales. The typewriters were ordered from the same distributor who handled the office machines. Because the manager felt it was too expensive to order each item separately, he had established a policy of placing an order to the distributor once a month. It took approximately one month for an order to be filled (i.e., typewriters ordered the first of this month would not be available to sell until the first of next month).

Because the typewriters had a high average unit cost, the manager of Epsilon was interested in keeping the inventory to a minimum. He estimated that every typewriter that he had remaining in inventory at the end of the month cost him $10. This figure was obtained by estimating the cost of capital tied up in inventory, cost of handling, and the alternative uses of space required.

On the other hand, each typewriter which he sold contributed approximately $50 profit and fixed costs. The manager estimated that of the customers who came into the store to buy a typewriter when he had none in inventory, half of them bought

## EXHIBIT I

### WEEKLY SALES RECORD

| Number of Typewriters Demanded during Week | Number of Weeks |
|:---:|:---:|
| 4 | 1 |
| 5 | 4 |
| 6 | 5 |
| 7 | 6 |
| 8 | 9 |
| 9 | 12 |
| 10 | 12 |
| 11 | 10 |
| 12 | 9 |
| 13 | 11 |
| 14 | 9 |
| 15 | 7 |
| 16 | 4 |
| 17 | 1 |
| 18 | 2 |
| 19 | 2 |

the machines elsewhere rather than waiting until Epsilon received a shipment.

It was almost impossible to predict what the weekly or monthly sales of typewriters would be. Fluctuations from week to week were apparently random, and there also appeared to be no increasing or decreasing sales trend over the two-year period during which records had been kept. A summary of the sales record is given in Exhibit I. From this he wondered if he could develop any policy regarding the number of typewriters to order each month.

# 16 Zeta Radio Company
*interaction of order point and order quantity*

The Zeta Radio Company manufactured short-wave radio receivers and transmitters. Many of the parts used were purchased from other companies.

The Zeta Company had fairly steady demand, largely because its principal customers were police and fire departments whose orders did not fluctuate with business conditions. The sales department had estimated sales of 25,000 combined receiver-transmitter units for the coming twelve-month period, and the production department had made its plans on this basis.

Inventory control on purchased parts had always been a problem at Zeta. For example, the inventory of one particular type of tube which was used in every transmitter was handled with a standard two-bin system. When the first bin was empty, a new order was placed. It happened, however, that the size of stock in the second bin and the size of the re-order quantity had been chosen arbitrarily and actual experience demonstrated that the second bin was *never* exhausted before the new order arrived.

Weekly usage, while averaging 500 tubes, was uneven because of unavoidable fluctuations in the rate of production. These fluctuations created a probability distribution of weekly usage which was estimated as shown in Exhibit I.

## EXHIBIT I

### USE OF THE TUBE

| Number of Tubes Used per Week | Relative Frequency of Use | Cumulative Frequency of Use of This Number or Less |
|---|---|---|
| 375 or less | .05 | .05 |
| 376 to 425 | .10 | .15 |
| 426 to 475 | .20 | .35 |
| 476 to 525 | .30 | .65 |
| 526 to 575 | .20 | .85 |
| 576 to 625 | .10 | .95 |
| Over 625 | .05 | 1.00 |

Order costs were $5 per order. Carrying costs per tube were $0.15 per month. There was a one-week lead-time between the issuance of an order and the receipt of the tubes.

Management was interested in inaugurating an inventory policy which would indicate order quantities, frequency of ordering, a safety stock so that there would be outages during the re-order period only one time in twenty, and the establishment of a re-order stock quantity to be used as the second bin.

# 17 Upsilon Chemical Company

*inventory control and simultaneous production scheduling*

The Upsilon Company produced bulk chemicals for industrial use. Most of the products were made in the same type of process on the same equipment. Slight differences in products, however, required changes in process settings and inputs between product runs and, in some cases, complete shutdown of the process was necessary.

Some time ago, the plant manager had ordered a study of the two or three products which accounted for the largest volume of sales. This study encompassed all areas of costs and sales. After completion of the study, it was hoped that the information could be used to develop better production and inventory policies.

Upsilon stored the finished products in containers in its own warehouse. As orders were received, the products were shipped to customers. Fast delivery was very important. A sample of forty days, chosen at random from records of the past year, showed that shipments of product M had a mean of 1200 gallons per day. The distribution about this mean is shown in Exhibit I. The standard deviation of the distribution is 200 gallons per day. Each gallon contributed $1.10 to profit and fixed costs.

The time required to set up the process to begin producing product M was twenty hours. Costs directly associated with set-up included materials, direct labor of the set-up crew, and idle time of the production crew. The total cost was $1200 per set-up.

The production process for product M took about twenty-eight hours (i.e., the first output of a run would begin twenty-eight hours after the run was started). Output was then continuous at a rate of 250 gallons per hour. Because the chemical process could not be interrupted, production was carried out on a twenty-four-hour day, seven-days-per-week basis.

A cost analysis showed that each gallon of product M accumulated $0.85 of variable costs by the time it reached finished-goods inventory.

## EXHIBIT I

### PROBABILITY OF DEMAND FOR PRODUCT M
### FROM A SAMPLE OF FORTY DAYS
### (DEMAND IN GALLONS PER DAY)

| Demand | Number of Days |
| --- | --- |
| Less than 800 | 1 |
| 800–900 | 2 |
| 900–1000 | 3 |
| 1000–1100 | 7 |
| 1100–1200 | 7 |
| 1200–1300 | 8 |
| 1300–1400 | 5 |
| 1400–1500 | 3 |
| 1500–1600 | 3 |
| More than 1600 | 1 |

There were a number of alternatives which demanded the limited funds which were available to management. The most profitable of these was a current project expected to yield a return on investment of about 30 per cent.

The period between the time a set-up was scheduled and the time the first output began was the most critical time as far as inventory shortages were concerned. Because other products required the same machines, it was necessary to schedule product M into production three days before set-up was begun. Management decided that during the total lead-time (scheduling, set-up, process time) demand could be allowed to exceed inventory only 7 per cent of the time.

1. Assuming that sales during the next year will follow the same pattern as given in Exhibit I (seven days a week), what size production run will minimize costs?

2. Assuming that management will risk stock-out in 7 per cent of the lead-times, at what inventory level should production be scheduled?

# 18 Nu Printing Company

*multiple item inventories*

The Nu Printing Company was a small concern which did mimeographing, multilithing, and offset printing work, primarily for local firms. Well over half of their work consisted of items covered by long-term contracts, such as company newspapers and newsletters.

The production manager was studying ways to cut costs and was concentrating first on the area of paper and ink inventories. He was able to separate most of the paper and ink into ten categories —six for paper and four for ink.

Based on past records and estimates for the next year, he projected the requirements for the next year for each of the ten categories. These estimates and the unit costs are tabulated in Exhibit I. The unit for paper was 500 sheets and the unit for ink was a 1-gallon container.

EXHIBIT I

ESTIMATED YEARLY REQUIREMENTS AND UNIT COSTS
FOR PAPER AND INK

| Categories | Unit Cost | Units Per Year |
|---|---|---|
| Paper A | $3.00 | 1000 |
| B | 3.50 | 2500 |
| C | 4.00 | 800 |
| D | 4.00 | 600 |
| E | 5.50 | 700 |
| F | 7.00 | 500 |
| Ink G | 10.00 | 40 |
| H | 10.00 | 10 |
| I | 7.00 | 15 |
| J | 12.00 | 10 |

The present policy regarding these items was to have a clerk initiate an order for new stock whenever the stock was down to a two- or three-day supply. This two- or three-day supply was based on his estimate of the usage rate. A one- or two-month supply was usually ordered. The order was then typed and recorded and usually telephoned to a local supply house. The Nu truck which delivered printing to customers would then go by and pick up the order and bring it to the plant. The truck was sometimes able to do this on the way to or from a customers. Other times, a special trip was required.

The production manager felt that this system left a good bit to be desired. The clerk who placed orders worked only part-time in the stock room, and sometimes he did not place the orders in time. This required a special trip by the truck and also usually resulted in delay in delivery of some of the printing work. Since the paper and ink were used at about the same rate throughout the year, the manager thought it might be possible to set up some simple inventory control system which minimized the chance of running out of an item, yet also kept costs to a low level.

One plan he considered was balancing inventory carrying costs with ordering costs for each item. He knew there was a policy of returning 20 per cent on money invested in current assets. He was not sure how much it cost to place an order, but, based on the time required to prepare the order and pick it up, he estimated $15 per order.

Since all of the items came from the same supply house, he wondered if it would be cheaper to order several different items at one time and, therefore, reduce the total number of orders and trips. Here again, he was not sure of costs, but he estimated the cost of ordering and handling all ten items on an order would be about $25.

1. Devise an inventory control system which will meet the requirements of the production manager.

# 19 Homepower Equipment Company

*multiple supply points*

The Homepower Equipment Company produced a line of power tools and accessories for home workshops. The various items ranged in size from a ¼-inch electric drill up to a large table saw and a wood-turning lathe. In addition to manufacturing and selling the original equipment, Homepower also produced and supplied replacement parts for this equipment.

The company stressed in its advertising its fast repair and replacement-part service, and, in order to guarantee this service, they maintained repair centers at each of their warehouses throughout their marketing area. There were six of these centers serving approximately the same number of customers. As the number of different products increased each year, it became a big problem to stock the right number of replacement parts for each item. The manager of the service and repair section decided to select some of the parts which were demanded often and see if he could develop some criteria regarding inventories of these items. One of the parts which he chose had been used in Homepower's largest selling item for the past five years. The manager examined the replacement-part records and sales for each year and talked to the design engineers about the expected life of the part. On the basis of these investigations, he found he could get a rough idea of the number of parts which would be demanded during a year. This figure was found by multiplying the estimates of the number of units in use at the beginning of the year in an area by the estimated average yearly usage in hours and dividing the product by the average life of the part. These data are summarized in Exhibit I.

On the basis of this information, the manager estimated the mean number of parts required per year. Since there was a two-month period needed to fill an order for more stock from a warehouse, he divided the mean by six to obtain a mean number of parts required per re-order period. He assumed that the distribution about this mean could be approximated by a Poisson distribution.

EXHIBIT I

## DATA FOR COMPUTING REPLACEMENT-PART REQUIREMENTS

| | |
|---|---|
| Estimated number of units in use in each of the six areas (areas served by the six warehouses) | 800 |
| Estimated life of the part | 100–110 hours |
| Estimated average usage of one unit each year | 30 hours |

The company had a policy that enough parts would be stocked at each location to meet demand 90 per cent of the time. While the manager was computing the stock necessary to meet this requirement at each station, it occurred to him that perhaps what the company should really try to do was to meet the demand of *all* stations 90 per cent of the time.

1. What stock should be on hand at each of the six locations in order that each location will meet the demand 90 per cent of the time?
2. What stock is satisfactory at each of the six locations in order that demand at all locations (total demand in the system) will be met 90 per cent of the time?

# 20 Sigma Tile, Incorporated

*inventory control and programming*

The Sigma Tile Company was located in the southwestern part of the United States. It produced floor tile, facing tile, and structural tile for the building industry and for the retail trade.

Facing tile and structural tile were similar in finish. Structural tile, however, was designed to take structural loads much like brick, whereas facing tile was merely attached to walls and had no load-bearing qualities in itself.

Sigma's sales were restricted to an area within a radius of about 400 miles of the plant because of the high shipping costs incurred by the heavy tile. The climate in Sigma's sales area permitted construction twelve months of the year. Hence, Sigma's sales were at a nearly constant rate throughout the year.


## PRODUCTION PROCESS

The first few steps of the production processes for the three types of tile were almost the same (see Exhibit I). Clay was ground and mixed to a fine powder. During this grinding and mixing, special materials were added to the mix, depending on the end product. For example, gritty substances such as carborundum or alundum were added to floor-tile mixes to give a nonslip surface. The powder was then transferred to the press department, where it was pressed into small squares, hexagons, and other geometrical shapes. After being pressed, the pieces were sent through a kiln where the shapes were vitrified or baked at a high temperature.

The kiln was a large brick structure heated by gas flames. A slow-moving conveyor passed through the kiln and carried the pressed powder while it was being baked. The baking process required between twelve and eighteen hours, depending on the characteristics of the material.

After being cooled, the floor tile was ready for use. Pieces were inspected, then pasted on sheets of paper, face down, to speed application, and the sheets were packed in boxes.

Facing tiles and structural tiles required additional processing. After the first firing in the kiln, the blanks resembled floor tile in appearance but were much more brittle. These blanks were called bisques. The bisques were then colored or painted and sent through a second kiln for glazing. The second kiln was similar to the first kiln except for temperature and conveyor speed. After being cooled from the glazing process, the small facing tiles were inspected and packed like floor tiles. Larger facing tiles and structural tiles were packed in boxes. Capacity of the inspection and packing department was almost unlimited, since semi-skilled labor could be obtained easily.

The company usually maintained an inventory of standard-

# EXHIBIT I

## PRODUCTION PROCESS FOR TILE

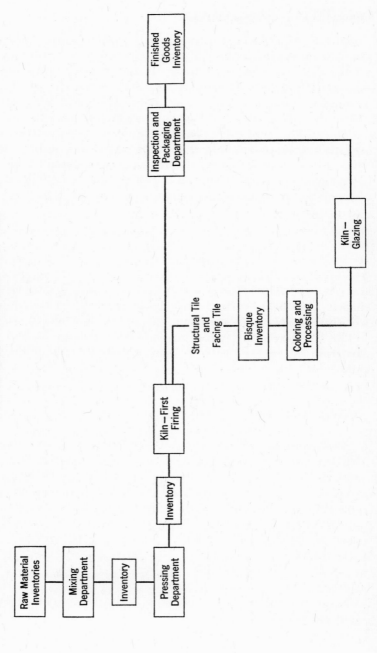

sized bisques for facing tiles and structural tiles. This was done in an effort to speed delivery of tile to customers. If a customer ordered a special color of a standard bisque, only glazing would be necessary and production time would be much shorter than it would if no bisques had been available. There had been increasing demands for colored tiles in the past several years.

Management had directed much effort toward the reduction of rejects but, because of the fragile nature of the tiles at times in the production process, a large percentage of rejects of some types still remained. The rejects were classified as seconds and could always be sold for about $0.10 per square foot. Current rejection rates were as follows:

|               |              |
|---------------|--------------|
| Floor tile    | 15 per cent  |
| Facing tile   | 20 per cent  |
| Structural tile | 10 per cent |

The percentages were based on the total run. For example, a run of 500,000 structural tiles could be expected to have 450,000 "first" and 50,000 rejects. The rejection rate was figured into the variable costs of the "firsts," so all of $0.10 per square foot was, from an accounting point of view, contribution to profits and fixed costs.

## SALES REQUIREMENTS

Most customers demanded almost immediate delivery of tile. Sigma offered twenty-four-hour delivery of all standard floor tiles and facing tiles. On some other facing tiles and some structural tiles, forty-eight-hour delivery was offered. It was possible to do this with tiles for which bisques had already been prepared. All other tiles had a five-day delivery committment. Sigma tried to meet all delivery dates since the sales group felt fast delivery was very important in getting and keeping customers. One sales executive said that he thought for every dollar of sales that Sigma could not make because of insufficient inventory, another dollar was lost within the next few months when the customer took his business elsewhere.

## COMPANY POLICIES

The company had a work year of fifty weeks. There was a plant-wide vacation during the last two weeks of July. Maintenance was performed on the kilns at this time.

Management had established a policy several years ago of earning 25 per cent on funds invested in current assets. Last year, they earned an average of 20 per cent on funds so invested. During the coming year, it was expected that the average return would probably be between 20 and 22 per cent although there were several individual projects which were expected to yield nearly 30 per cent.

At the June meeting of the company's executive committee it had been decided that an effort would be made toward, "running this company scientifically," as the president phrased it. The executive committee planned to analyze products, processes, sales, and costs and then to direct the next year's operations toward keeping costs down and maximizing profits.

By late October, data had been assembled by the sales, accounting, and production departments. These data are presented in Exhibits II through VII. Only a little more than a week remained until the executive committee held its next meeting. At this meeting, a proposal covering product mix, inventory, and scheduling policies for the next year was to be presented.

## EXHIBIT II

### PRODUCTION CAPACITIES—MIXING AND PRESSING [a]

| | Time Available | Percentage of Productive Time [b] | Capacity of Each Department |
|---|---|---|---|
| Mixing department | 8 hours/day 5 days/week | 80 | 33,000 lb hour [c] |
| Pressing department | 8 hours/day 5 days/week | 85 | floor tile 2800 square feet/hour or facing tile 2800 square feet/hour or structural tile 2400 square feet/hour |

[a] There were three identical mixers in the mixing department and two identical presses in the press department. The mixers and presses could be scheduled independently of one another.

[b] The percentage was computed from production records of the past year. It was found by dividing the actual output by the capacity and averaging the result. The capacity was measured by multiplying the capacity per hour by the number of hours worked by the mixing department.

[c] One cubic foot of mix weighed approximately 130 pounds. For planning purposes, a pound of mix may be assumed to make a pound of tile. Tile was usually measured in units of square feet. This measure referred to the one side that would be visible when the tile was in use. The average thicknesses of tiles produced by Sigma were as follows:

| | |
|---|---|
| Floor tile | 1 inch |
| Facing tile | 1.50 inches |
| Structural tile | 2.40 inches |

## EXHIBIT III

### CHARACTERISTICS OF KILNS

| | | |
|---|---|---|
| Total time required for first firing, per piece | | |
| Structural and facing tile | 12 hours | 2000°F |
| Floor tile | 18 hours | 2500°F |
| Total time required for glazing | | |
| Structural and facing tile | 24 hours | 2500°F |
| Capacity of each kiln | 10,000 square feet | |
| | of tile | |

*Note:* The two kilns were almost identical in construction and either could be used for first firing or glazing. A kiln could not be used to fire and glaze at the same time, nor could it be used to fire floor tile and either of the other two types simultaneously. The time required to change the temperature of a kiln 500°F was six hours. Any tile blanks which were moving through the kiln during this time would be unusable even as seconds. The conveyor speed could be changed in only a few minutes. Kilns operated twenty-four hours a day, seven days a week. During the two-week vacation in the summer, routine repairs were made on them.

## EXHIBIT IV

### RAW MATERIAL COSTS

Cost of 1 ton of clay—          $10
     no quantity discounts are offered

Clay was the main raw material for the tile. Other constituents accounted for only a small percentage of the cost.

## EXHIBIT V

### SELLING PRICES AND COSTS OF PRODUCTION [a]
### (IN DOLLARS PER SQUARE FOOT)

| Process | Floor Tile | | Facing Tile | | Structural Tile | |
|---|---|---|---|---|---|---|
| | Process Costs | Cumulative Total | Process Costs | Cumulative Total | Process Costs | Cumulative Total |
| Mixing department | | | | | | |
| Material | 0.054 | | 0.081 | | 0.130 | |
| Other costs | 0.028 | | 0.036 | | 0.033 | |
| Total | 0.082 | 0.082 | 0.117 | 0.117 | 0.163 | 0.163 |
| Pressing department | 0.013 | 0.095 | 0.015 | 0.132 | 0.014 | 0.177 |
| First firing | 0.037 | 0.132 | 0.027 | 0.159 | 0.027 | 0.204 |
| Second firing (glazing) | | | 0.042 | 0.201 | 0.042 | 0.246 |
| Inspection and packing | 0.018 | 0.150 | 0.015 | 0.216 | 0.014 | 0.260 |
| Selling price | 0.29 | | 0.425 | | 0.545 | |

[a] These costs, furnished by the accounting department, include only variable costs. Included are such items as direct labor, supervision, a portion of power and gas, maintenance, and rejects—all of which are assumed to vary directly with the production level.

## EXHIBIT VI

### SET-UP TIMES AND COSTS

| | |
|---|---|
| Mixing department | |
| Cost of changing a mixing machine from one type of tile mix to another | $200 |
| Time required | 3 hours |
| Pressing department | |
| Cost of changing a press from one type of tile form to another | $90 |
| Time required | 1 hour |
| Purchasing department | |
| Cost of processing an order to a supplier | $12 |

## EXHIBIT VII

### SALES ESTIMATES AND REQUIREMENTS [a]

| Type of Tile | Estimates |
|---|---|
| Floor tile | 1.8 million square feet. Steady demand, almost entirely for standard units. |
| Facing tile | 1.2 million square feet. Steady demand. Sizes, colors, and glazes fairly well known for 25% of estimated sales. Sizes known for an additional 50%. Uncertain of sizes, glazes, and colors for 25%. |
| Structural tile | 900,000 square feet. Relatively steady demand throughout year. Colors and glazes unknown. Sizes known for 50% of estimated sales. |

[a] Sales estimates are for "firsts" only.

# part IV Dynamic Programming Problems

## 21 Tau Products Company
*dynamic programming*

The Tau Products Company, a manufacturer of milling machines, was contemplating the introduction of a new machine on the market. Because of competing products, the sales department estimated that the selling price, net of any discounts, would drop after the first few months. After the machines became established on the market, the price would rise somewhat. The production department estimated they could cut production costs considerably within a year so that the total product cost per machine would drop from $10,700 to $9000. Because of warehouse limitations, no more than ten completed units could be stored. A summary of sales and production is given in Exhibit I.

The inventory at the beginning of period A was zero, and the inventory at the end of period H should be zero. Anything pro-

EXHIBIT I

| Time Periods | Selling Price (thousands of dollars) | Product Cost (thousands of dollars) | Plant Capacity (in units) |
|---|---|---|---|
| A | 11.0 | 10.7 | 5 |
| B | 11.0 | 10.5 | 7 |
| C | 10.5 | 10.5 | 10 |
| D | 10.3 | 10.5 | 15 |
| E | 10.2 | 10.0 | 20 |
| F | 10.0 | 9.5 | 20 |
| G | 10.3 | 9.0 | 20 |
| H | 10.5 | 9.0 | 20 |

duced within a period could be sold in that period or held in inventory until the next period. Because of modifications and obsolescence, any inventory at the end of one period had to be sold during the period immediately following.

1. Use dynamic programming to approach the problem, and develop a general expression to be maximized in each time period.
2. Solve for the production, inventory, and sales in each period.
3. What is the total profit for the eight periods?

# 22 Rho Machine and Foundry Company
*dynamic programming*

The Rho Machine and Foundry Company produced a variety of metal parts from cast aluminum. The company cast the blanks in their own foundry and did all of the necessary machining in their own machine shop. Each product which the company produced went through the same general production process.

In late May, the executive committee met to plan operations for the next fiscal year. The committee consisted of the president and the other three officers of the company—the sales manager, production manager, and treasurer.

The Rho Company sold most of its output to companies in one industry. The level of Rho's activity depended almost entirely on activity of that industry which varied from year to year but followed a consistent seasonal pattern. Based on experience and on industry estimates for the next year, the sales manager projected Rho's sales. This projection, by months, is shown in Exhibit I.

EXHIBIT I

ESTIMATE OF SALES DEMAND
(THOUSANDS OF DOLLARS)

| | |
|---|---|
| July | $410 |
| August | 435 |
| September | 460 |
| October | 485 |
| November | 515 |
| December | 530 |
| January | 535 |
| February | 540 |
| March | 520 |
| April | 490 |
| May | 450 |
| June | 420 |

Although the volume of sales could be estimated fairly accurately, it was almost impossible to estimate the product mix. Past experience had shown that it was too expensive to try to guess the mix and produce ahead of time. Because of this, the company operated as a job shop and produced only on order.

The company had recently completed a cost analysis aimed at determining how costs varied at different levels of production. The analysis group found that there were: (1) some costs which remained fixed regardless of production level; (2) other costs which seemed to vary directly with production level; and (3) costs which at low levels of production increased proportionately slower than the production level but at high volumes increased proportionately faster than the production level.

Since total revenue from sales was directly proportional to

sales (and production level), contribution to fixed costs and profit could be calculated by subtracting the type 2 and type 3 costs from revenue at any level. Contribution at a number of levels was calculated and plotted to yield the S-shaped curve in Exhibit II.

EXHIBIT II

CONTRIBUTION FROM SALES TO FIXED COSTS AND PROFIT AT DIFFERENT PRODUCTION LEVELS

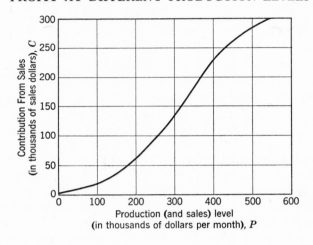

The production manager, who had some experience with mathematical programming, tried to convert this data into a form which lent itself to programming techniques. He decided to make the following approximations about the data in Exhibit II:

(1)         $0 \leqslant P \leqslant 150,\quad C = 0.2P$

(2)         $150 \leqslant P \leqslant 300,\quad C = 0.69P - 74$

(3)         $300 \leqslant P \leqslant 600,\quad C = 300 - \dfrac{(P - 600)^2}{534}$

where $P$ was the production in thousands of dollars and $C$ was the contribution in thousands of dollars. [Expressions (1) and (2) are linear approximations, while the quadratic expression of (3) is a parabola with its vertex at $P = 600$.]

In addition to costs incurred while the company operated at a given level, there were costs associated with changing the production from one level to another. When the production level was increased, there were hiring, training, and plant rearrangement costs. When the production level was decreased, there were lay-off costs and plant rearrangement costs.

The cost of increasing production level was estimated to be some constant times the square of the difference between production in the present month, $P_m$, and production in the preceding month, $P_{m-1}$, where $P_m$ and $P_{m-1}$ were measured in thousands of dollars. This constant was 0.01. Thus

$$(4) \qquad 0.01(P_m - P_{m-1})^2 = \text{Cost in thousands of dollars of increasing production level.}$$

The cost of decreasing production was less than that of increasing production and was estimated to be 0.01 times the difference in production. Thus

$$(5) \qquad 0.01(P_{m-1} - P_m) = \text{Cost in thousands of dollars of decreasing production level.}$$

In past years, management had tried to meet all sales demand. Now that the cost data were available, they wondered if analysis might indicate that it would be more profitable to meet only a portion of the demand, especially when demand increased rapidly from month to month.

The production costs and production-level-change costs were the only ones over which management felt they could exercise control during the year. The sales manager said that he did not believe that failure to supply demand would affect any future sales to any customer.

Current production was at a rate of $393,000 per month.

1. Write a general expression that will express the net contribution for each month.

2. Derive an expression that will give the optimum monthly production during periods of increasing sales demand.

3. What should monthly production be during periods of decreasing sales demand?

4. Keeping in mind that all production must be sold within the same month (production cannot be greater than sales in any given month), how much should be produced each month in order to maximize contribution over the year?

5. Suppose that in October, when production was at a level of only $465,000, it became apparent that industry activity would be generally lower than originally predicted and the revised sales pattern of Rho was given by the following:

| | | | |
|---|---|---|---|
| November | 490 | March | 500 |
| December | 515 | April | 470 |
| January | 520 | May | 440 |
| February | 520 | June | 400 |

How would the revised estimates affect the decisions which were based on the initial data?

# part V Queuing Problems

## 23 Eta Airlines
*single channel queuing*

Eta Airlines ran nonstop trips from several cities to Washington. The Washington airport was frequently congested, and their planes were forced to fly in the "stack" over the field awaiting the landing of other planes which had arrived previously. Management was interested in determining the length of time their planes would have to wait so that an adequate amount of fuel could be loaded prior to departure to cover both the intercity flying time and the flying time in the "stack." At the same time, the company did not want to load an excessive amount of fuel since the pay load would be reduced.

The rate of arrival of planes in Washington varied with the hour of the day. The arrival rate was greatest between the hours of 4 and 5 p.m., and Eta chose this time period for an initial study since experience showed that this was when the "stack" time was the greatest.

Studies made in Washington showed that the mean arrival rate for the hour being studied was twenty planes per hour, or one every three minutes. It had also been determined that there was variance about this mean—due to flight cancellations, charter, and private flights, etc.—which could be described by a Poisson distribution.

During clear weather the Washington tower could land one plane per minute, or sixty an hour. When the weather was bad and landings had to be controlled from the ground, the landing rate was reduced to thirty per hour. Both of the landing rates were actually mean rates, and the distribution around the means could also be approximated by Poisson distributions. Eta's flights were short enough so that it could generally tell prior to take-off whether ground-controlled landings would be required in Washington. For safety reasons, the landing rates could not be significantly increased if the number of planes in the "stack" increased.

When a plane ran short of fuel while in the "stack," it was given priority to land out of order. Airport rules, however, made it clear that this was not to be relied on by the airlines being served, and Eta had decided to carry enough fuel so that they would have to take advantage of the priority no more than one time in twenty.

Specifically, Eta wanted to know:

1. How large the "stack" would average in good weather and in bad weather?

2. How long a plane would be in the "stack" and process of landing in good and bad weather.

3. How much "stack" and landing time to allow for so that priority to land out of order would have to be requested only one time in twenty.

# 24 Phi Oil Company

*multiple channel queuing*

The Phi Oil Company, a small regional concern, was constructing a new service station on a highway soon to be finished. In determining the number of pumps to install, the traffic analysis department took data from past records of stations with similar characteristics and location. Along with traffic estimates for the new highway, the department estimated that customers' arrivals over most of the day would approximate a Poisson distribution with a mean of thirty automobiles per hour. They expected these rates to remain about the same from a few months after the highway's opening through the next two or three years. Previous studies showed that one pump could service a mean of ten automobiles per hour, with the service time distribution approximating a Poisson.

Since the company was involved in a large construction program at the time, they wished to maximize the return on investment in each station. This meant construction of the minimum facilities consistent with good service. Based on the automobile arrival rates and service rates per pump, the company decided that three pumps would be sufficient to handle customers for the next several years.

During the first six months of operation, the station manager noticed that quite often lines began to form at the pumps. Furthermore, it appeared to him that some people who would have otherwise stopped for gasoline saw the lines and took their business elsewhere. The net result was that the station did less business than had been previously estimated. The manager checked the automobile arrival rates, adjusting them upward somewhat for the business he felt was bypassing his station because of the lines. He also checked the service rates of the pumps. Both of these rates, he found, were almost exactly what the estimates had predicted.

Since the predicted and actual figures matched so closely, the

manager was quite puzzled about the discrepancy between predicted and actual performance.

1. What is the probable explanation of the long lines and loss in business?
2. If four pumps had been installed, what would have been the probability that an arrival would have to wait in line?
3. Further investigation showed that people did not enter a service
   station if they believed they would have to wait more than four
   minutes for service. If four pumps had been installed at this station,
   would the average waiting time have been less than this?
4. With four pumps, what would have been the average total time
   (waiting plus service) in the station?
5. With four pumps, what would have been the average number of
   automobiles waiting and being serviced?
6. With four pumps, approximately what percentage of the time would
   one particular pump not be in use?

# 25 Iota Equipment Company

## *multiple stage queuing and Monte Carlo analysis*

The Iota Equipment Company specialized in the rebuilding of
automotive and marine engine parts. Parts were received in
batches in the late evening or early morning. The batches were
processed and rebuilt during the day and shipped back to customers within twenty-four hours of receipt if possible.

One particular component was received in a group and was
processed in smaller batches through departments A, B, and C in
that order. Analysis of past records indicated that the number of
units received each day was distributed in a random manner with
a mean of 1100 and a standard deviation of 200.

The number of units processed in each department each day
varied randomly. Analysis showed that all the variation could be
explained by the differences in processing rates on the individual

machines in each department. For example, studies indicated that each of the four machines in department A processed units at a mean rate of 290 per eight-hour day but that there was a normal distribution around the mean with a standard deviation of fifty units per day. This was a completely random distribution. No other factors such as backlog of units or processing rates of other machines or departments seemed to affect an individual machine's processing rate. A summary of processing characteristics and costs is given in Exhibit I. The hourly cost was incurred regardless of the machine's output, and a minimum of eight hours' cost was incurred each day irrespective of the work load.

## EXHIBIT I

### PRODUCTION CHARACTERISTICS AND COSTS

|  | Department | | |
|---|---|---|---|
|  | A | B | C |
| Number of machines | 4 | 2 | 2 |
| Average output per machine (in units per working day) | 290 | 590 | 570 |
| Standard deviation per machine (units per day) | 50 | 100 | 50 |
| Cost per hour of operating each machine | $4 | $7 | $8 |

The batches were small enough and the work schedules of the three departments were staggered sufficiently so that no working time was lost in departments B and C between the start of the first batch through department A and starting it through the other two departments.

Since the units flowed through the three departments, the slowest department on a particular day determined the number of units which could be processed. This might lead to a case where department C was capable of processing units at a high rate but was limited by a bottleneck in department A or B. Department C would then have to work overtime in order to process the units produced by department A or B or both in overtime.

Since the company stressed fast service to its customers and since storage space was limited, management had established a policy of overtime so that all work could be processed on the same day that it was received. Operation on overtime cost 50 per cent more than the regular hourly costs. Processing rates for each machine on overtime were approximately the same as the rates during that particular day.

The manager of the group which included departments A, B, and C was interested in reducing costs. He was puzzled by the fact that the average output of each department was greater than the average number of units received each day, yet each department frequently requested overtime. He wondered if fast service to customers really justified the costs.

In addition to a decision on overtime, the manager was considering the purchase of additional machines for departments which seemed to be frequent bottlenecks. The costs for the three types of machines were $2000 for department A, $3000 for department B, and $4000 for department C. Operating costs would be the same as for the present machines. Immediate delivery of the machines was promised by the manufacturers. The manager estimated that the new machines would have an economic life of about three years during which time the volume of operation and the costs of the processes would remain relatively fixed.

1. Analyze three weeks (fifteen working days) of the company's operation, with and without overtime.

2. How much is the policy of overtime costing the company?

3. What machines (if any) should be purchased?

# 26 Rutledge-Warren Company

## *a more complicated queuing and servicing problem*

The Rutledge-Warren Company operated a group of stores in several of the southeastern states. These stores sold a complete line of furniture, appliances, auto parts, hardware, and home and farm supplies.

The assistant manager of one of the larger stores had recently become interested in the use of quantitative techniques in store operation. One of the first areas to which he applied these techniques was that of inventory control. He had instituted an analysis of sales and inventory in several departments and, from the results, was able to show the department managers how they could increase their inventory turn and in some cases actually increase sales. He planned eventually to have all departments studied, and he hoped that all would be able to operate with a faster inventory turn.

Another general area which interested him was the size of the departmental sales forces. He had observed at times that a good many of the sales personnel of each department were idle and other times that there were so many customers in a department some would refuse to wait for service and leave.

Throughout most of the year each department operated with the same size sales force. On Friday evenings and Saturdays and during special seasons such as Christmas, however, additional personnel were sometimes hired on a part-time basis to help handle the increased sales. On other occasions regular store personnel worked overtime. This was possible since the store was open sixty hours a week, and the regular-time work week was only forty-four hours. Personnel were given mornings, afternoons, and sometimes whole days off in addition to an hour for lunch so that they were regularly available for selling only forty-four hours a week.

Each department manager had considerable latitude in regard to scheduling overtime for the sales force. Decisions for additional sales personnel were usually made by the store manager and usually involved hiring more personnel for all departments. There were nearly always questions regarding the amount of overtime, when it was needed and when extra sales personnel were needed. The department managers were responsible for each of their departments as profit centers, and they did not wish to incur overtime costs and costs of extra personnel unless extra sales justified it. On the other hand, they did not wish to lose potential sales. Many of the department managers felt that customers liked the merchandise and good service at Rutledge-Warren and that some customers shopped there as many as forty to fifty times a year.

The number of customers served each day and the rate of service varied among departments. Because of this, each department's sales force had to be determined separately. Several years ago a study had been made of the relationship between customers served each day and the number of sales personnel needed. The number of customers who shopped in each department was divided into the total time that the department was open. This gave the average time between customer arrivals. The amount of time required to serve a customer was also studied. This was expressed in minutes as an average service time per customer. The average service time per customer divided by the customer arrival rate rounded off to the next highest integer gave the minimum number of sales personnel needed in the department. Store management realized that this number was not realistic since customer arrival rate was greater in the middle of the day than at the beginning or end. Consequently they had increased the figure by 80 to 100 per cent as a safety margin. This method was currently used to estimate the number of sales personnel needed during regular days, special seasons, and on Fridays and Saturdays. Decisions for overtime and additional sales personnel were made on this basis.

The assistant manager felt that application of the present method actually resulted in an arbitrary number of sales personnel in each department and that this number in most cases was much higher than necessary. He decided to study one department and, if he could improve its operation, he would extend analysis to others. He felt a department not dealing in style or seasonal goods would be easiest to start with and, on this basis, chose the hardware department.

He outlined his plan to the hardware manager, and they decided to study the department on a Saturday, which was one of the heavier sales days.

The four-hour period between 11:30 and 3:30 was chosen. Two clerks were borrowed from other departments for the study. One devoted his entire time to keeping a record of the number of customers in the department at all times. This was done on a long strip of paper with time plotted across the horizontal axis and number of customers plotted on the vertical axis. Each time a customer entered, the clerk drew a vertical line to the next higher level indicating another customer had entered the department at a particular time. Each time a customer left, the clerk dropped a line to the next lower level. A sample of the record is shown in Exhibit I. The clerk also tried to note any customers who left without being served.

### EXHIBIT I

### A PORTION OF THE RECORD OF THE NUMBER OF CUSTOMERS IN THE DEPARTMENT AT ANY TIME

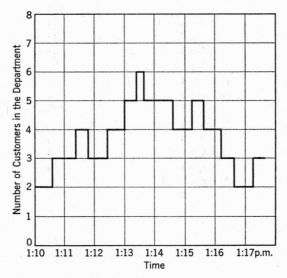

The second clerk divided his time between two jobs. One was a study of the time required for a clerk to wait on a customer.

This time included time spent with the customer while helping him make his selection and time required to register and complete the sale if a sale were made. The other was a study of the relationship between time spent in the department and size of purchase.

After the study was made, the assistant manager checked the data. It appeared to him that there was no increasing or decreasing sales trend during the four-hour period. He then grouped the data into time between customer arrivals and time that a given number of people were in the department. These data are summarized in Exhibits II and III. He also grouped the data on

## EXHIBIT II

### TIME BETWEEN ARRIVALS
### GROUPED DATA FOR THE FOUR-HOUR PERIOD

| Time between Arrivals (in minutes) | Number |
|:---:|:---:|
| 0 –0.2 | 31 |
| 0.2–0.4 | 32 |
| 0.4–0.6 | 23 |
| 0.6–0.8 | 21 |
| 0.8–1.0 | 19 |
| 1.0–1.2 | 11 |
| 1.2–1.4 | 14 |
| 1.4–1.6 | 8 |
| 1.6–1.8 | 6 |
| 1.8–2.0 | 9 |
| 2.0–2.2 | 6 |
| 2.2–2.4 | 4 |
| 2.4–2.6 | 5 |
| 2.6–2.8 | 4 |
| 2.8–3.0 | 4 |
| 3.0–3.2 | 3 |
| More than 3.2 | 10 |

service time per customer. This is shown in Exhibit IV. In these cases he assumed that there was no variance in service time among different salesmen. A study of the sales per customer

## EXHIBIT III

### TIME THAT *n* NUMBER OF CUSTOMERS WERE IN THE DEPARMENT DURING THE FOUR-HOUR PERIOD

| Number of Customers *n* | Time (in minutes) |
|---|---|
| 0 | 16.8 |
| 1 | 35.5 |
| 2 | 52 |
| 3 | 49 |
| 4 | 29.3 |
| 5 | 18.8 |
| 6 | 13.6 |
| 7 | 9.6 |
| 8 | 5.8 |
| More than 8 | 9.6 |

## EXHIBIT IV

### SERVICE TIME FROM A RANDOM SAMPLE OF THIRTY-ONE

| Service Time (in minutes) | Number from Sample |
|---|---|
| Less than 1 | 5 |
| 1–2 | 7 |
| 2–3 | 6 |
| 3–4 | 4 |
| 4–5 | 2 |
| 5–6 | 3 |
| 6–7 | 1 |
| 7–8 | 1 |
| 8–9 | 1 |
| 9–10 | 0 |
| More than 10 | 1 |

*Note:* The total serving time for the sample of thirty-one was 101 minutes.

showed no correlation between dollar sales and the amount of time spent in the department or between dollar sales and the particular salesmen. Sales were made to 193 persons and the mean sale was $2.30. There were four sales people in the hardware department for the entire four hours.

The clerks noted that a few people left the department without being waited on. During the four hours, eighteen people were observed to do this. Most of these occurred when there were more than six people already in the department.

The assistant manager wanted to answer the following questions:

1. Can the number of customers at a given time be estimated with any degree of accuracy?
2. Should the number of clerks in the hardware department be increased to five, left at four, or reduced to three? The minimum pay of a part-time clerk who could give the same service as the other four clerks was $2.75 per hour, and he would have to be hired for a minimum of eight hours on Saturday.

# 27 Electronautics Corporation

*another complicated queuing and servicing problem*

The administrative engineer of the electromechanical group of the Electronautics Corporation was helping the manager of the group prepare the operating budget for the next year. Electronautics did research, development and production work on electronic, pneumatic, hydraulic, and mechanical components and systems for the aircraft and missile industry. Some typical components were amplifiers, solenoid valves, actuating cylinders, and high-speed pumps, which were used in missile guidance, launching, and control, and air-induction control systems. The electromechanical group did whatever electromechanical work was needed for Electronautics' contracts. The group also received subcontracts from other companies for study and development work, usually on advanced types of components.

Part of the budgeting was concerned with the drafting department. This department prepared drawings from engineers' sketches, vendor drawings, and physical objects themselves. These drawings were used in layout work, installation, and specification control and for contract proposals. The drawings could be classified into three general categories, A, B, and C. The A drawings were the smallest and usually required the least amount of drafting time. They were usually drawings of components. The B drawings were somewhat larger and took more time than the A's. They included most of the subsystem and schematic drawings. The C drawings were the largest and required the most drafting time. They were usually installation and system drawings, although some of the more complicated subsystem drawings fell in this category.

Since the drafting department supported the engineering groups, an estimate of engineering work load could be used to give a rough idea of the amount of drafting time which would be needed. This was satisfactory for yearly planning, but it did not seem to work well for weekly or even monthly operations. During the past year, the drafting supervisor had noted that his department sometimes had a large backlog of drawings. On the other hand, as much as 50 per cent of the department would occasionally be without work. The supervisor felt that the trouble was due to the way drafting requests were received from the engineering groups. Some days a large number of requests were received while other days only a few came in. There appeared to be no pattern to the number of requests received from day to day. Since engineering was most anxious to get drawings completed as fast as possible, it was often necessary to schedule an appreciable amount of overtime.

In the last group meeting, the group manager, his subgroup managers, and the drafting department supervisor had discussed the problem of service from the drafting department. Since the subgroup managers each were charged a portion of the drafting department's operating expenses, they were interested in keeping the department's costs as low as possible consistent with good service. They finally agreed upon the following: For A drawings, mean time in the drafting department should not exceed two days and only 15 per cent of the drawings should require more than five days. For B drawings, mean time in the drafting department should not exceed four days, and only 15 per cent of the drawings should require longer than eight days. For C drawings, mean time in the department should not exceed six days and only 15 per cent of the drawings should require more than ten days.

The engineering work load for the next year was expected to

### EXHIBIT I

#### NUMBER OF DRAWINGS RECEIVED ON EACH OF TWENTY-FIVE DAYS CHOSEN AT RANDOM

| Day Designation | A Drawings | B Drawings | C Drawings |
|---|---|---|---|
| 1 | 6 | 2 | 2 |
| 2 | 8 | 6 | 0 |
| 3 | 8 | 3 | 0 |
| 4 | 10 | 1 | 0 |
| 5 | 12 | 3 | 2 |
| 6 | 8 | 3 | 0 |
| 7 | 12 | 2 | 0 |
| 8 | 9 | 3 | 1 |
| 9 | 14 | 2 | 0 |
| 10 | 9 | 7 | 0 |
| 11 | 15 | 4 | 1 |
| 12 | 5 | 4 | 0 |
| 13 | 4 | 4 | 1 |
| 14 | 11 | 1 | 3 |
| 15 | 13 | 1 | 0 |
| 16 | 11 | 5 | 1 |
| 17 | 9 | 3 | 1 |
| 18 | 10 | 2 | 0 |
| 19 | 16 | 0 | 1 |
| 20 | 7 | 4 | 1 |
| 21 | 7 | 1 | 1 |
| 22 | 13 | 5 | 1 |
| 23 | 10 | 5 | 0 |
| 24 | 11 | 2 | 0 |
| 25 | 9 | 3 | 2 |

remain about the same as it had been during the past year, so the administrative engineer first decided to check the rate at which the different drawings were received in the department. He chose twenty-five days at random from the past year, and, from the drafting department's record of drawings received, he tabulated the number of A's, B's, and C's received on each of these days. The results are shown in Exhibit I.

The department kept no record of the drafting time required for the drawings. Each draftsman did record on his daily time card the amount of time charged to each drawing. Time cards were available for the last two weeks, so the administrative engineer took a sample of twenty A drawings and twenty B drawings and took all of the nine C drawings executed within the last two weeks. From them, he computed the mean times and also grouped the distribution of drafting times for each of the three drawing types. They are shown in Exhibits II, III, and IV.

### EXHIBIT II

#### DRAFTING TIMES FOR A SAMPLE OF
#### TWENTY A DRAWINGS
(in hours)

| Time Required | Number of Drawings |
|---|---|
| 0–2 | 3 |
| 2–4 | 5 |
| 4–6 | 5 |
| 6–8 | 3 |
| 8–10 | 1 |
| 10–12 | 0 |
| 12–14 | 1 |
| More than 14 | 2 |
| Mean time = 6 hours | |

Before he could study the department any further, he thought he must answer the following two questions:

1. Do the drawings received each day conform to any predictable pattern?

2. Do drafting times conform to any pattern?

## EXHIBIT III

### DRAFTING TIMES FOR A SAMPLE OF
### TWENTY B DRAWINGS
(in hours)

| Time Required | Number of Drawings |
|:---:|:---:|
| 0–5 | 3 |
| 5–10 | 5 |
| 10–15 | 5 |
| 15–20 | 3 |
| 20–25 | 1 |
| 25–30 | 1 |
| 30–35 | 1 |
| 35–40 | 1 |

Mean time = 14.3 hours

## EXHIBIT IV

### DRAFTING TIMES FOR A SAMPLE OF
### NINE C DRAWINGS

| Time Required | Number of Drawings |
|:---:|:---:|
| 0–15 | 2 |
| 15–30 | 3 |
| 30–45 | 1 |
| 45–60 | 1 |
| 60–75 | 1 |
| 75–90 | 1 |

Mean time = 36 hours

If he found that there were patterns for number of drawings received and drafting times, he would then answer the following questions:

3. Assuming that the drafting department is divided into three groups, each of which works on only one size drawing, how large must each group be in order to meet the drafting-time conditions agreed upon by the managers?

4. Could the number of draftsmen in the department be reduced if the department was operated as one group where everyone did all three types of drawings?

# part VI Replacement Problems

## 28 Crescent Insurance Company
*items that deteriorate*

The Crescent Insurance Company maintained a computing room in its acturial department. The room contained, among other equipment, twelve desk calculators.

The company contracted with a local business to keep the machines in good operating condition. Breakdown became more frequent as the machines aged, and the contract reflected this fact. The servicing company charged $72 per year to service a calculator up to one year old, $124 per year for a calculator from one to two years old, the cost increasing by $52 for each additional year of age. Under the terms of the contract, payment was made for previous year's service on the anniversary date of the acquisition of the machines.

The insurance company was interested in devising a policy for calculator replacement. The manufacturer was asked to inspect the existing machines and to indicate how much would be allowed in trade-in value if the old calculators were replaced with new ones. The new machines would be the same model as

the old ones and the price, before trade-in was deducted, was
$1000 per machine.

Trade-in values allowed by the manufacturer are shown in
Exhibit I. The manufacturer stated that at least $100 would be
allowed on any trade-in, regardless of the age of the machine
traded. In the case of the calculators shown in Exhibit I, how-

EXHIBIT I

TRADE-IN ALLOWED ON OLD CALCULATORS

| Calculator | Years Since Purchase | Trade-In Allowed (dollars) |
|:---:|:---:|:---:|
| A | 1 | 725 |
| B | 1 | 675 |
| C | 2 | 525 |
| D | 2 | 500 |
| E | 3 | 325 |
| F | 4 | 270 |
| G | 4 | 285 |
| H | 4 | 280 |
| I | 5 | 215 |
| J | 5 | 200 |
| K | 6 | 175 |
| L | 7 | 125 |

ever, even though age was the principal factor used in arriving
at the trade-in allowance, several other factors associated with
the condition of the machines were also considered.

One of the employees in the actuarial department agreed to
search for a formula which would express trade-in values as a
function of time. He discovered that a frequently used general
expression is;

$$L_t = S + \frac{C - S}{K^t},$$

where $L_t$ = trade-in value at end of year $t$
      $C$ = original cost of equipment
      $S$ = terminal salvage value of equipment
      $t$ = age of equipment in years
      $K$ = an unknown constant

He decided to experiment to see if a value for $K$ could be found which, used in the equation, would approximate the trade-in allowances of the manufacturer. If this was successful, he would then construct a model to find the optimum replacement policy for the calculators. He was instructed to include a "cost of money" in his work of 10 per cent compound interest per year.

# 29 Suburbia Electric Company

*items that fail*

The Suburbia Electric Company generated and distributed electricity. It began operations in 1955. The company approximately doubled its entire operations in 1960 with the opening of a new subdivision of houses.

Suburbia installed 5000 utility poles in January 1955. Since then it had replaced the poles as they failed. A study made by

EXHIBIT I

PER CENT OF UTILITY POLES EXPERIENCING
FAILURE DURING VARIOUS YEARS AFTER
INSTALLATION

| Year after Installation | Per Cent of Poles Failing |
|---|---|
| First year | 1 |
| Second year | 2 |
| Third year | 3 |
| Fourth year | 5 |
| Fifth year | 7 |
| Sixth year | 12 |
| Seventh year | 20 |
| Eighth year | 30 |
| Ninth year | 16 |
| Tenth year | 4 |
| Total | 100 |

the company showed a life expectancy of poles as shown in Exhibit I. No poles were expected to last more than ten years.

Suburbia's experience up to early 1960 was in accord with this study. Of the 5000 poles installed in January 1955, fifty were replaced during the next twelve months, 100 during the next year, etc. By January 1960, only 4100 of the original 5000 poles were still in use. Some of the poles put in as replacements during the period 1955 through 1959 had themselves been replaced.

In January 1960, Suburbia installed 5000 additional poles to extend service to the new subdivision. It also installed 361 poles to replace failures. Records of the company showed installations as indicated in Exhibit II. The number of poles still in use in January 1960 is shown in Exhibit III.

### EXHIBIT II

#### NUMBER OF POLES INSTALLED

| Date of Installation | Number Installed |
|---|---|
| January 1955 | 5000 |
| February 1955–January 1956 | 50 |
| February 1956–January 1957 | 101 |
| February 1957–January 1958 | 152 |
| February 1958–January 1959 | 255 |
| February 1959–January 1960 | 5361 |

### EXHIBIT III

#### NUMBER OF POLES IN USE, JANUARY 1960

| Date of Installation | Number of Poles |
|---|---|
| January 1955 | 4,100 |
| February 1955–January 1956 | 44 |
| February 1956–January 1957 | 96 |
| February 1957–January 1958 | 147 |
| February 1958–January 1959 | 252 |
| February 1959–January 1960 | 5,361 |
| | 10,000 |

The pattern of replacement installations which was developing suggested that more attention should be paid to forecasting the replacement demand for coming years. No one in the Suburbia Company anticipated any significant changes in the size of its operations so that planning could be based on the assumption that a 10,000 pole system would be maintained in the future and that installations would be made only to replace old poles.

Exhibit IV provides cost information.

## EXHIBIT IV

### COSTS ASSOCIATED WITH INSTALLING POLES

| | |
|---|---|
| 1. Purchase price of a pole | $50.00 |
| 2. Inventory carrying costs per pole per year | 5.00 |
| 3. Cost of placing an order and making payment for poles | 20.00 |
| 4. Cost of replacing individual poles on failure | 20.00 |
| 5. Installation cost per pole if 5000 or more are replaced in a group | 16.00 |

# part VII Analysis of Variance

## 30 Theta Machine Shop
*simple analysis of variance*

The Theta Machine Shop had a job requiring precision drilling on an unusually hard steel alloy. It was using five drill presses for the job and discarding bits after each had been used for ten holes.

Exhibit I shows a sample of the extent to which the holes varied from the specified diameter. The shop wanted to know:

1. Whether the variance was caused more by the order of drilling or by the press being used?
2. Whether using each bit only five times would significantly reduce the variance?

EXHIBIT I

INSIDE DIAMETERS OF HOLES, MEASURED IN TENS OF
THOUSANDTHS OF INCHES FROM SPECIFIED DIAMETER

| Order of Drilling | Drill Press | | | | |
|---|---|---|---|---|---|
| | A | B | C | D | E |
| 1st | +2 | +2 | +5 | −3 | +4 |
| 2nd | +3 | 0 | +2 | −1 | +1 |
| 3rd | +4 | +9 | +7 | +9 | −1 |
| 4th | +4 | +6 | +9 | −2 | +5 |
| 5th | −9 | −1 | +2 | +5 | +3 |
| 6th | −0 | −5 | −5 | −7 | −4 |
| 7th | −8 | −7 | −4 | +1 | −4 |
| 8th | −8 | −2 | −3 | −1 | +3 |
| 9th | +6 | −4 | +5 | 0 | −2 |
| 10th | 0 | −4 | −8 | −8 | −3 |

# 31 Pi Industries

## *three-factor analysis*

The management of Pi Industries was troubled about the high
rejection rate of parts produced in the turret lathe department.
The production manager was assigned the task of investigating
the problem and reporting his findings at the next weekly meeting of the management council.

Since he had only a week in which to study the problem, the
production manager was quite limited in his methods of attack.
He guessed that poor quality and, hence, rejections could be
ascribed to three main causes: (1) machines, (2) operators, and
(3) job. There were a number of old machines in the turret lathe
department. Their replacement had been considered for some

time, but, since there were many other demands for funds and since the machines still worked, replacement had been postponed. These machines might not be capable of working to close tolerances. A variance among operators might be expected. Age, ability, and pride of workmanship would affect the quality of product. Third, the job specifications, characteristics, and tolerances would affect the rejection rate.

There were records available for every job which had been performed in the past year. These records listed, among other things, the machine, the operator who had performed the job, and the rejection rate. The production manager examined the records and chose two jobs which had been performed by three different men on three different machines during the past year. He realized that a study of broader scope and with samples in each category instead of single entries would have more meaning. Not only did the time available limit the scope, but, since Pi Industries was primarily a job shop and only about 30 per cent of their work was of a recurring nature, it was hard to find enough similar combinations of men, machines, and jobs for analysis.

He assembled the data in Exhibit I and hoped to draw some tentative conclusions from an analysis of them.

## EXHIBIT I

### REJECTION RATES FOR JOBS (IN PER CENT)

| | | Operators | | | | | |
| | | A | | B | | C | |
| | Jobs | x | y | x | y | x | y |
|---|---|---|---|---|---|---|---|
| Machine | 1 | 3 | 11 | 15 | 13 | 15 | 18 |
| number | 2 | 4 | 11 | 7 | 5 | 3 | 7 |
| | 3 | 17 | 30 | 5 | 10 | 9 | 12 |

# 32 Summit Fabrics *

## Latin square design

The Summit Fabric Company produced cotton cloth primarily for the apparel industry. The major part of the output was poplin, broadcloth, and denim, but recently the company had become interested in fabrics for the "wash-and-wear" market.

One problem which had been encountered with the wash-and-wear materials was the ease with which the fabrics tore after several washings. The characteristics of the yarn, weave, and finish in these fabrics accelerated wear-out in comparison with other cloth. As part of Summit's research program, studies were being made of the quantitative effects of different warp yarn twists, filling yarn twists, and finishes on the launderability of the cloth.

Warp yarns are the longitudal strands in the woven fabric. Filling yarns are the interlacing or crosswise strands. During spinning operations, the yarns are given a certain amount of twist to give them more strength. Generally filling yarns are given less twist to avoid kinks in weaving, and consequently they are fuller and not as strong as warp yarns.

Finishing operations give the cloth special properties and effects. These operations include pre-shrinking, glazing, starching, and calendering.

The company had developed standard laundering tests. Samples were washed in water under controlled conditions of temperature, agitation, mineral content, and detergent concentration. After each washing the cloth was dried, and a sample was tested by subjecting it to tension. The tension was increased until the sample tore, and this value of tension was recorded. As samples of a type of cloth were subjected to more and more washings, the tension required to tear them decreased. When the tension required to tear did not exceed a certain limit, the fabric was said to have worn out.

* This problem was suggested by N. L. Enrick, Director of Operations Research, Institute of Textile Technology, Charlottesville, Virginia.

The fabric research group was preparing to order samples of wash-and-wear fabrics for analysis of twists and finishes. There were four specific finish variations in which they were interested. There were numerous choices of warp and filling yarns for the desired weave, but four values for each were chosen as representative of the ranges of interest. To prepare samples of all the combinations for yarn twists and finishes would require sixty-four different fabrics. This number could be reduced to sixteen by using a Latin square design of the experiment. The fabric research group designed an experiment which conforms to the plan in Exhibit I.

The results of the test are shown in Exhibit II.

## EXHIBIT I

### LATIN SQUARE DESIGN FOR LAUNDERABILITY TEST

| Finish | Warp Yarn Twist | | | |
|--------|-----|-----|-----|-----|
|  | W | X | Y | Z |
| 1 | A * | B | C | D |
| 2 | C | D | A | B |
| 3 | D | A | B | C |
| 4 | B | C | D | A |

* A, B, C, and D are filling yarn twists.

## EXHIBIT II

### RESULTS OF LAUNDERABILITY TEST
### (NUMBER OF WASHINGS BEFORE WEAR-OUT)

| Finish | Warp Yarn Twist | | | |
|--------|-----|-----|-----|-----|
|  | W | X | Y | Z |
| 1 | 36 | 30 | 33 | 42 |
| 2 | 28 | 42 | 47 | 36 |
| 3 | 45 | 53 | 41 | 43 |
| 4 | 34 | 38 | 37 | 58 |

1. What is the significance of each factor in the launderability test?

# 33 Chi Electronics

*Graeco-Latin square design*

Chi Electronics produced electronic equipment for industrial and military markets. Included in their product line were individual items such as amplifiers and oscillators and also systems for control, telementry, and infrared detection.

One of the company's largest-selling items was an industrial process controller. An important part of this controller was a high-gain amplifier which amplified a small error signal to a sufficient power level to operate indicators and valves which acted to correct the error in the process. Reliability and ease of maintenance were very important. A faulty unit might cause the loss of everything in the process at the time of failure. Ease of maintenance permitted operating personnel to check and repair the unit promptly and to restore control before the process went too far off.

For many years the company had constructed its amplifiers on an aluminum chassis similar to those used in television and radio. With the advent of printed circuit boards, engineers were considering changing to these. A printed circuit board differed from an aluminum chassis in that, instead of wiring components together, the circuit was actually printed or etched in metal on a board and components were mounted on the top of the board. The bottom of the board was dipped into a bath of molten solder which adherred to the circuit and the component leads. Production was much faster with the boards than with conventional chassis, but usually only large production runs justified the expense of preparing a "master" for the particular board. There were two intermediate alternatives between the aluminum-chassis construction and the printed circuit board. One was a terminal board on which components were soldered in a parallel line between two lines of lugs with wires connected between the proper lugs. The other was a board similar to the printed circuit board on which components were mounted, but, instead of using a printed circuit, wire connections were made between the components.

Another major change under consideration was the shift from vacuum-tube circuits to those using transistors. Transistors, in general, exhibited a higher level of reliability. Both tubes and transistors were available in "Better Quality" and "Good Quality," the "Good Quality" being cheaper in both cases.

In addition to the two proposed changes, there were important considerations of resistor tolerance and voltage regulation. Commercial resistors were available with a 20 per cent positive and negative tolerance. For example, a 1000-ohm resistor might be anywhere between 800 and 1200 ohms. Ten per cent, 5 per cent, and 1 per cent tolerances were available, but they cost much more. The design department tried to design circuits which would accommodate the full 20 per cent limits without degradation in performance. Comparison tests were sometimes run on otherwise identical units constructed with; (1) all resistors at the negative 20 per cent limit; (2) all resistors at the positive 20 per cent limit; (3) all resistors within 1 per cent of mean value; and (4) random selection of values within the positive and negative 20 per cent limits.

In regard to voltage, the supply voltage affected the components and the characteristics of the amplifier. Excessively high voltages could cause components to burn out, and low voltages might not allow satisfactory circuit operation. Effects of intermittent fluctuations in voltage were important since in the actual installations large fluctuations were sometimes present.

The design engineering department was confronted with the need to get information about the effects of voltage, resistor tolerance, mounting, and transistor and tube performance. Of particular interest was the operating life, or the time to failure, of the amplifier. The company usually conducted accelerated life tests on its products to help estimate this time. Accelerated life tests consisted of operating a unit at high levels of vibration, temperature, duty cycle, etc., so that several years of normal life might be simulated in less than one year. Measurements were made on the unit under test at periodic intervals.

When the unit failed to function within specified limits, failure was said to occur. A record was made of the elapsed time between start of the test and time of failure.

To test all combinations of resistor values, mounting, voltage, and transistors or tubes one time would require 256 units. This was far too many units to test to failure. Some other method was needed which would require fewer units but yield as much information. After considering the problem for a while, one of the engineers came up with a scheme as shown in Exhibit I. With only sixteen units, he proposed to get the same information on individual variables that would be available from 256 unit tests. He admitted that possible interaction between variables could not be analyzed, but these interactions would be present in the residual error, and further tests on the suspected interactions could be conducted.

Each one of the sixteen blocks in Exhibit I specifies the con-

EXHIBIT I

DESIGN FOR AMPLIFIER LIFE-TEST EXPERIMENTS *

| | | Mounting | | |
|---|---|---|---|---|
| | | Printed Circuit Board | Aluminum Chassis | Terminal Board with Wired Connections | Mounting Board with Wired Connections |
| R e | Nominal value | $X_1$ N | $X_2$ H | $T_2$ L | $T_1$ F |
| s i | Random mix | $X_2$ L | $X_1$ F | $T_1$ N | $T_2$ H |
| s t | +20 per cent limit | $T_2$ F | $T_1$ L | $X_1$ H | $X_2$ N |
| o r s | −20 per cent limit | $T_1$ H | $T_2$ N | $X_2$ F | $X_1$ L |

* Meaning of Symbols:
$X_1$  Better quality transistors
$X_2$  Good quality transistors
$T_1$  Better quality vacuum tubes
$T_2$  Good quality vacuum tubes

N  Normal voltage
H  High voltage
L  Low voltage
F  Fluctuating voltage

struction and test procedure for one amplifier. For example, the lower right-hand square specified that an amplifier constructed with "Better Quality" transistors, with resistors at 20 per cent less than their nominal value and mounted on a board with wired connections will be given an accelerated life test at a low supply voltage. Units were constructed and tests were run. The results of the tests are shown in Exhibit II.

EXHIBIT II

RESULTS OF AMPLIFIER LIFE TESTS TIME TO FAILURE
(IN HOURS)

| | | Mounting | | | |
| --- | --- | --- | --- | --- | --- |
| | | Printed Circuit Board | Aluminum Chassis | Terminal Board with Wired Connections | Mounting Board with Wired Connections |
| R e | Nominal value | 8100 | 5200 | 4400 | 4100 |
| s i | Random mix | 6400 | 6800 | 5300 | 4100 |
| s t | +20 per cent limit | 4900 | 6200 | 4900 | 5400 |
| o r s | −20 per cent limit | 4200 | 4300 | 5600 | 7500 |

1. Through an analysis of variance, determine the influence of each factor on operating life.

# 34 Xi Laboratories

*three-factor analysis*

Xi Laboratories was an environmental testing laboratory which specialized in the evaluation of components under extremes of temperature, humidity, vibration, acceleration, etc. Much of their business came from the government and from missile and aircraft manufacturers. Under a typical contract, Xi was furnished components and was requested to test the units for satisfactory operation and make recommendations regarding the use of the components in subsystems and systems.

The company had recently received a contract from a large aircraft engine manufacturer to conduct a series of tests on pressure switches. (A pressure switch is basically an electrical switch which is actuated when a pneumatic or hydraulic pressure exceeds a preset limit. The switch is usually connected in some kind of warning or control circuit.) The manufacturer was preparing for production of a new engine, and several pressure switches were needed for each engine.

The switches were to be mounted on the engine assembly. Hence, they would be subjected to vibration while the engine was in operation. In addition, the switches would have to operate in temperatures ranging from $-65°F$ to $+180°F$.

The aircraft engine manufacturer had narrowed its choice of pressure switch vendors to three—A, B, and C. The manufacturer had furnished a number of each of these units to Xi Labs. All three vendors produced switches which were nearly identical in size, shape, and weight. Each switch was in the form of a cylinder about 5 inches long and 2 inches in diameter with the electrical connection at one end and a pressure connection at the other. The axis of the cylinder was designated the $Z$ axis.

The engineer in charge of the testing contract planned to test three units of each switch. The units would be tested under combinations of three temperatures and three conditions of vibration. Temperatures to be used would be: (1) $70°F$, or room temperature; (2) $-65°F$; and (3) $+180°F$. Conditions of vibration would be (1) no vibration; (2) vibration along the Z axis; and (3) vibration perpendicular to the Z axis. Since the switch was symmetrical perpendicular to the Z axis, it was satisfactory to test the switch along only one of the perpendicular axes, which was designated the X axis.

The tests were conducted by mounting one of each model (A, B, C) on the vibrator or "shaker." A variable pressure source and an electric indicating circuit were connected to the switch. A "hot–cold" box was placed over the switch on the "shaker," and tests were begun. In each temperature and vibration test the pressure was increased slowly from o p.s.i. and, when the switch actuated, a technician recorded the pressure which was indicated by a gage connected to the pressure connection of the switch. The sequence was then repeated twice, each time with a new set of A, B, and C components. Results are shown in Exhibit I.

## EXHIBIT I

### ACTUATION PRESSURES
### (IN POUNDS PER SQUARE INCH)

|  |  | Switch Model | | | | | | | | |
|---|---|---|---|---|---|---|---|---|---|---|
|  |  | A | | | B | | | C | | |
|  | Vibration | X Axis | Z Axis | o | X Axis | Z Axis | o | X Axis | Z Axis | o |
| T | $T_1$: −65°F | 210 | 208 | 206 | 208 | 208 | 208 | 216 | 208 | 210 |
| E |  | 217 | 202 | 201 | 215 | 207 | 205 | 212 | 207 | 205 |
| M |  | 210 | 205 | 200 | 210 | 203 | 204 | 209 | 211 | 208 |
| P |  |  |  |  |  |  |  |  |  |  |
| E | $T_2$: +70°F | 206 | 198 | 198 | 200 | 200 | 200 | 197 | 196 | 194 |
| R |  | 201 | 202 | 207 | 205 | 200 | 194 | 200 | 200 | 198 |
| A |  | 207 | 207 | 200 | 196 | 196 | 198 | 200 | 201 | 198 |
| T |  |  |  |  |  |  |  |  |  |  |
| U | $T_3$: +180°F | 200 | 189 | 184 | 195 | 180 | 191 | 193 | 190 | 186 |
| R |  | 202 | 196 | 191 | 198 | 183 | 189 | 198 | 193 | 193 |
| E |  | 200 | 192 | 195 | 193 | 186 | 188 | 199 | 192 | 189 |

After completion of the tests, it was necessary to determine the effects on the switches of temperature, vibration, mounting axis, and any combination of these. In addition, it was necessary to determine if there was any significant difference among the switches of the three different suppliers.

# part VIII Miscellaneous Problems

## 35 Mu Capacitor Company
*sequencing*

The Mu Capacitor Company manufactured capacitors for the electronics industry. Capacitors, together with other components such as resistors, transformers, tubes, and transistors, are used in radio, T.V., and other electronic circuits. Capacitors are required in a wide variety of sizes, materials, and ratings in order to meet the requirements of many different types of varied circuits.

The Mu Company produced two types of capacitors: (1) paper and wax type, and (2) electrolytic type. The fabrication processes were quite different for the two types. Because of that, the company had established two separate manufacturing groups. As a rule, orders for paper and wax type were for large numbers of different varieties, whereas orders for electrolytics were for only one or two types.

On a particular Friday, the production managers were individually faced with the problems of scheduling the next week's production in order to meet the end-of-week delivery dates.

The production manager for the paper and wax group had orders for ten different types. The orders would have to be processed in ten batches (no splitting of orders) through three machines, A, B, and C in that sequence The times required on each machine for each order are summarized in Exhibit I. Times

EXHIBIT I

## PRODUCTION TIMES FOR ORDERS IN PAPER
## AND WAX DEPARTMENT
## (IN HOURS)

| | Machines | | |
|---|---|---|---|
| Order Number | A | B | C |
| 1 | 5 | 1 | 4 |
| 2 | 6 | 4 | 7 |
| 3 | 4 | 3 | 6 |
| 4 | 5 | 2 | 4 |
| 5 | 4 | 2 | 5 |
| 6 | 2 | 2 | 4 |
| 7 | 6 | 3 | 6 |
| 8 | 5 | 4 | 6 |
| 9 | 5 | 3 | 6 |
| 10 | 5 | 2 | 4 |

include processing time, set-up time, and transportation time between machines.

The manager wished to arrive at an optimum scheduling which would minimize the total time required to complete the ten orders.

The production manager for the electrolytic department was faced with a somewhat different scheduling problem. He had orders for two different types of capacitors. The two orders had to be processed on different machines but not in the same sequence. A summary of the machines and machine times per order is shown in Exhibit II.

The production manager wanted to schedule the work so as to minimize the time between the start of the first job and the completion of the last job.

## EXHIBIT II

### SEQUENCES AND TIMES FOR THE TWO ELECTROLYTIC ORDERS
### (IN HOURS)

| | | Machines | | | | | | | |
|---|---|---|---|---|---|---|---|---|---|
| | | A | B | C | D | E | F | G | |
| Order | 1 | 2 | 5 | 6 | 5 | 7 | 4 | 2 | |
| | | A | C | D | B | E | F | H | G |
| Order | 2 | 3 | 4 | 6 | 4 | 5 | 4 | 7 | 2 |
| Alternate routing for order 2 | | A | C | D | B | F | E | H | G |
| | | 3 | 4 | 6 | 4 | 4 | 5 | 7 | 2 |

1. Determine the optimum scheduling for the paper and wax capacitors. If the company works a forty-hour week, will any overtime be needed to complete the orders?
2. Determine the optimum scheduling for the electrolytic capacitors, and find the total elapsed time.

# 36 Omega Company

*routing*

The Omega Company produced nonferrous metal products for industrial and consumer markets. The company operated its own foundry in which it cast the products. The pieces then were placed in boxes or on pallets and taken by a fork-lift truck to the machining department where operations were performed on the cast blanks by lathes, milling machines, and drill presses.

## OPERATIONS AFTER LEAVING THE MACHINING DEPARTMENT

After the blanks had been machined, they were sent to different departments. A few were sent directly to the final assembly, inspection, and packaging department. Most of the others were sent to the painting department where the desired type of finish was applied or to the subassembly department. After painting was completed, units went to the subassembly department or the final assembly, inspection, and packaging department. Output from the subassembly department went to the final assembly, inspection, and packaging department or to the painting department.

## SCRAP

The company made an effort to keep scrap to a minimum. Scrap originated mostly because of defective castings. Most of the defective castings were detected and discarded before they left the foundry, but some were not found until they had reached the machining department. A much smaller number were not detected until they had reached the subassembly department.

## SCHEDULING

Since all products did not follow the same flow, the problem of moving boxes and pallets from one department to another was one which demanded a great deal of attention. The present method was for the fork-lift operator to check the routing tag on each box or pallet and then take them to their destination. The operator would check at that destination to see if any units were ready to be moved elsewhere. If there were none, he would check at some other department or cruise around until he was paged by the production control supervisor to go to pick up a load.

This system was unsatisfactory in several respects. Quite often boxes and pallets of units would build up at one department while another department would have no units to work on. The fork-lift operators would have to work overtime in order to transfer all units to the proper places so work could begin in the departments the next day.

## EXHIBIT I

### CHARACTERISTICS OF FORK-LIFT TRUCKS

| | |
|---|---|
| Maximum number of boxes or pallets which could be carried at one time | 7 |
| Average number carried by each truck during the past year (during regular working hours) | 3¾ |

## EXHIBIT II

### ESTIMATED NUMBER OF BOXES AND PALLETS WHICH WOULD BE READY TO BE MOVED BETWEEN DEPARTMENTS EACH HOUR *

| Between Departments –and– | | Mean (per hour) | Standard Deviation |
|---|---|---|---|
| 1 | 2 | 25.0 | 2.0 |
| 2 | 3 | 12.5 | 1.7 |
| 3 | 4 | 15.0 | 1.7 |
| 4 | 5 | 10.0 | 1.5 |
| 2 | 4 | 9.5 | 0.9 |
| 2 | 5 | 2.5 | 0.7 |
| 3 | 5 | 11.9 | 1.6 |
| 4 | 3 | 14.4 | 1.8 |

* Based on production records of the past year, adjusted for delivery difficulties in the past year.

*Note:* There was no apparent relationship between the figures for one department and those of another, even when examined with respect to lag times.

One solution would be to add more fork-lift trucks to the existing fleet of six; however, the production control supervisor felt that some better method of scheduling would alleviate the problem. Accordingly, he collected the data in Exhibits I, II, and III. By analyzing them he hoped to develop some better schedule for the trucks.

## EXHIBIT III

### AVERAGE TIMES REQUIRED TO MOVE BETWEEN DEPARTMENTS

| Between Departments –and– | | Average Time * (in minutes) |
|:---:|:---:|:---:|
| 1 | 2 | 10 |
| 2 | 3 | 10 |
| 3 | 4 | 10 |
| 4 | 5 | 10 |
| 2 | 4 | 13 |
| 2 | 5 | 17 |
| 3 | 5 | 15 |
| 4 | 3 | 10 |
| 5 | 4 | 4 |
| 3 | 1 | 6 |
| 5 | 1 | 15 |

* The average time includes a rest allowance for the operator. For the first eight routes, it also includes an average loading and unloading time.

# 37 Baker Paint Company
## *location of facilities*

The Baker Paint Company was a large national concern which produced and marketed through hardware stores and lumber companies and its own retail outlets a large line of inside and outside paints. In order to guarantee two-day delivery to customers, Baker operated a number of warehouses and a fleet of trucks.

In one particular part of the country, sales had reached the point where management believed a new warehouse was necessary. There were a number of factors which had to be considered in locating a new warehouse. The most important one, however, was the total gallon-miles traveled from warehouse to customers since total costs correlated quite closely to this figure. The company figured that it cost an average of $0.15 to ship 1000 gallons of paint one mile. The cost included gasoline, oil, maintenance for the outward trip and the return trip from the customer when the truck would be empty.

For each customer in the area, the present annual sales volume and growth rate were computed and yearly sales estimates were made for each of the next five years. These estimates were averaged and the resulting figure was entered on the map in Exhibit I near the geographical location of the customer.

## EXHIBIT I

## LOCATION AND ESTIMATED YEARLY DEMAND
## (IN THOUSANDS OF GALLONS)
## OF BAKER'S CUSTOMERS

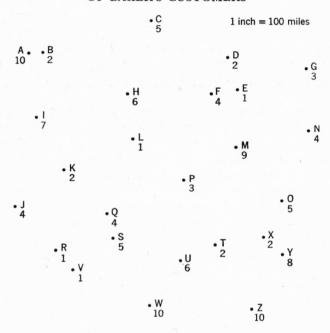

1 inch = 100 miles

1. On strictly gallon-miles considerations, where should the new warehouse be located?

# appendix  References to Instructional Materials

This appendix is a reference guide to instructional material helpful in the solution of the problems. To conserve space, the following abbreviations are used.

| AUTHORS AND BOOKS | ABBREVI-ATIONS |
|---|---|
| 1. Vazsonyi, A., *Scientific Programming for Business and Industry*, John Wiley and Sons, New York, 1958. | AV |
| 2. Bowman, E. H., and R. B. Fetter, *Analysis for Production Management*, Richard D. Irwin, Homewood, Illinois, 1957. | BFA |
| 3. Bowman, E. H., and R. B. Fetter, *Analyses of Industrial Operations*, Richard D. Irwin, Homewood, Illinois, 1959. | BFD |
| 4. Churchman, C. W., R. L. Ackoff, and E. L. Arnoff, *Introduction to Operations Research*, John Wiley and Sons, New York, 1957. | CAA |
| 5. Cochran, W. G., and G. M. Cox, *Experimental Designs*, 2nd ed., John Wiley and Sons, New York, 1957. | CC |
| 6. Wilson, E. B., Jr., *An Introduction to Scientific Research*, McGraw-Hill, New York, 1952. | EBW |
| 7. Grant, E. L., *Principles of Engineering Economy*, The Ronald Press, New York, 1950. | ELG |
| 8. Ferguson, R. O., and L. F. Sargent, *Linear Programming*, McGraw-Hill, New York, 1958. | FS |

| AUTHORS AND BOOKS | ABBREVI-<br>ATIONS |
|---|---|
| 9. Terborgh, G., *Dynamic Equipment Policy*, McGraw-Hill, New York, 1949. | GT |
| 10. Kurnow, E., G. J. Glasser, and F. R. Ottman, *Statistics for Business Decisions*, Richard D. Irwin, Homewood, Illinois, 1959. | KGO |
| 11. Moroney, M. J., *Facts From Figures*, Penguin Books, London, 1957. | MJM |
| 12. Morse, P. M., *Queues, Inventories, and Maintenance*, John Wiley and Sons, New York, 1958. | PMM |
| 13. Bellman, R., *Dynamic Programming*, Princeton University Press, Princeton, N.J., 1957. | RB |
| 14. Reinfeld, N. V., and W. R. Vogel, *Mathematical Programming*, Prentice-Hall, Englewood Cliffs, N.J., 1958. | RV |
| 15. Metzger, R. W., *Elementary Mathematical Programming*, John Wiley and Sons, New York, 1958. | RWM |
| 16. Gass, S. I., *Linear Programming Methods and Applications*, McGraw-Hill, New York, 1958. | SIG |
| 17. Vajda, S., *Readings in Linear Programming*, John Wiley and Sons, New York, 1958. | SV |
| 18. Sasieni, M., A. Yaspan, and L. Friedman, *Operations Research—Methods and Problems*, John Wiley and Sons, New York, 1959. | SYF |
| 19. Whitin, T. M., *The Theory of Inventory Management*, Princeton University Press, Princeton, N.J., 1957. | TMW |

# Reference Guide

| Problem | References Abbreviation | References Chapter |
|---|---|---|
| Alpha Manufacturing Company | CAA | 11 |
| | SYF | 8 |
| | FS | 2 |
| | RWM | 2 |
| | RV | 2 |
| | SP | 2 |
| | SIG | 10 |
| | AV | 2 |
| | BFA | 5 |
| Psi Metal-Working Company | CAA | 11 |
| | FS | 3 |
| | RV | 3 |
| | RWM | 2 |
| Beta Machine Products Company | CAA | 11 |
| Lambda Fertilizer Company | SYF | 8 |
| Southern Cotton Mill | FS | 4, 5 |
| Kappa Manufacturing Company | RV | 5 |
| Taylor and Lockhart Farm | RWM | 3 |
| Sierra Mills, Incorporated | SV | 14, 17 |
| | SIG | 2, 4 |
| | AV | 4 |
| | BFA | 4 |
| Gamma Valve Company | CAA | 12 |
| Omicron Airfreight Company | SYF | 8 |
| Delta Machine Tool Department | FS | 7 |
| | RWM | 4 |
| Bravo Manufacturing Company | CAA | 8 |
| Lynchburg Foundry Company | SYF | 4 |
| Epsilon Office Supply | TMW | 3 |
| Zeta Radio Company | AV | 10 |
| Upsilon Chemical Company | BFA | 9, 10 |
| Nu Printing Company | BFD | 24 |
| Homepower Equipment Company | | |

| Problem | References | |
|---|---|---|
| | Abbrevi- ation | Chap- ter |
| Sigma Tile, Incorporated | CAA | 8, 12 |
| | SYF | 4, 8 Appendix III |
| | FS | 4, 5 |
| | RV | 5 |
| | RWM | 3 |
| | TMW | 3 Appendix 5 |
| | SV | 14, 17 |
| | SIG | 2, 4 |
| | AV | 4, 10 |
| | BFA | 4, 9, 10 |
| Tau Products Company | SYF | 10 |
| Rho Machine and Foundry Company | AV | 8 |
| | BFA | 5 |
| | RB | 1 |
| Eta Airlines | CAA | 14 |
| Phi Oil Company | SYF | 6 |
| Iota Equipment Company | PMM | 3, 4, 11 |
| | BFB | 15 |
| Rutledge-Warren, Incorporated | CAA | 14 |
| Electronautics, Incorporated | SYF | 6 |
| | DMM | 4 |
| | BFB | 14, 15, 17 |
| | BFA | 11 |
| Crescent Insurance Company | CAA | 17 |
| Suburbia Electric Company | SYF | 5 |
| | GT | 3, 4, 5, 6, 7, 8 |
| | ELG | 16 |
| Theta Machine Shop | BFA | 8 |
| Pi Industries | CC | 2, 3, 4, 5 |
| Summit Fabrics | MJM | 19 |
| Chi Electronics, Incorporated | EBW | 8 |
| Xi Laboratories | | |
| Mu Capacitor Company | CCA | 16 |
| | SYF | 9 |
| Omega Company | BFA | 11 |